C. - MC

INTERNATIONAL SERIES OF MONOGRAPHS ON
ELECTRONICS AND INSTRUMENTATION
GENERAL EDITORS: D.W. FRY AND W. HIGINBOTHAM

VOLUME 30

ELECTRICAL ANALOGUES
OF PIN-JOINTED SYSTEMS

Electrical Analogues of Pin-jointed Systems

Edited by

K. K. KEROPYAN

Translated by

VERA GARFIELD

Translation edited by

D. P. ATHERTON

Lecturer in Electrical Engineering,
University of Manchester

A Pergamon Press Book

THE MACMILLAN COMPANY
NEW YORK

CONTENTS

PREFACE

MANY present-day problems of structural mechanics take a considerable time to solve and often slow up work unnecessarily. Much has been written with the object of simplifying the usual methods of calculation, principally, in connection with plane and three-dimensional multi-stage frameworks. But in the great majority of cases these methods still leave the designer and constructor with the job of carrying out tedious and difficult numerical work.

Recently, newly-developed computing techniques have provided new methods for solving certain of these problems and so relieving the designer of much complicated calculation. Electrical analogues, which during the last decade or so have been introduced into many spheres of science and technology, have also been used to solve problems concerned with structures.

Today, the principles of electrical analogues, giving simpler and more rapid solutions of static and dynamic structural calculations, are well established. Much work on this has been done by the scientists of the Rostov-on-Don Civil Engineering Institute (RISI), under Prof. K.K. Keropyan, and by the Taganrog Radiotechnical Institute (TRTI), under Prof. G.Ye. Pukhov.

The fundamental aim of the work of both institutes was to establish analogies between bent beam equations arising in building mechanics, and the network equations of certain electrical circuits. It was proved that a three terminal, 'T' shaped, active electrical network was the electrical analogue of a bending rod, being described by similar equations. This led to the construction of an electrical analogue EMSS-1 for calculations of plane rod systems. Measurement of the voltages

vii

and currents in the electrical circuit equivalent to the framework to be analysed enabled, with the help of scaling coefficients, the angles of deflection and the bending moments in the rods of the system to be found. Some of the results were published under the title *Electrical analogues of beams and frames* (Taganrog 1956).

The present volume includes contributions from members of both institutes, developing and generalizing the ideas of the Taganrog collection.

One section is concerned with the statics, the second with the dynamics, of buildings.

In the article by K. K. Keropyan, "Static solution of a twisted thin-walled rod under load using an electrical analogue", we shall see that the three terminal active electrical network can be the analogue of a thin-walled rod of open or closed profile twisting under load. This has enabled designers to solve a wide range of torsion problems with the help of the electrical analogue built by G.Ye. Pukhov and O.V. Il'enko, to solve problems of bending based on this type of circuit.

In a second article by the same author, "Electrical analogues of some plane rod systems", an electrical circuit is described that is analogous to the deformations and the moments of transverse stresses at an arbitrary section of a bending rod with constant and variable rigidity.

A third article, also by Keropyan, describes a new circuit equivalent to a static framework, enabling the stresses in all parts of the framework to be calculated from the magnitudes of the currents flowing in the branches of the network.

The article of S.Ya. Sadetov, "Formula of bi-moments in initial parameters", brings a new aspect of the formula of bi-moments in initial parameters, which can be made use of in solving the questions of constrained torsion of thin-walled rods of an open profile using either electrical analogue or usual methods.

The article by O.V. Il'enko and V. I. Usynin, "Electrical analogue EMSS-1 for the design of beams and frameworks" describes the analogue constructed at the laboratory of TRTI for the Rostov Civil Engineering Institute.

The article by V. I. Usynin, "The use of iteration in analogues of frameworks with the help of four terminal networks", discusses an iterative method used in solving a number of structural problems with the help of the Pukhov–Il'enko analogue. This analogue also makes it possible to solve problems of frameworks with displaced joints.

The title of O.V. Il'enko's paper, "Calculation of the effects of temperature on beams and plane frameworks using electrical analogue circuits", is self explanatory.

The article of P. M. Chegolin, "An electrical circuit simulating a complicatedly bent conical beam", describes a four terminal active network used to simulate a beam bent by forces causing contraction or stretching.

A second article by the same author, "Comparison of the methods of building dynamics and those used in the evaluation of electrical circuits", points out similarities between some of the methods of calculations used in elastic dynamic systems, and methods of linear calculations used in electrical circuits.

P. M. Chegolin's third article, "Electrical analogues of equations with finite differences used in calculating bent rods", describes an active electrical network for simulating a bent rod system described by finite difference equations. By using this analogue we can solve various problems of dynamics such as, forced poly-harmonic oscillations, bending-torsion oscillations, etc.

The article of Ye. Pukhov and O.V. Il'enko, "The calculation of deflection of pillars' foundations with the help of electrical analogues of frameworks", describes formulae used in determining magnitudes of resistances for simulating building on elastic foundations.

In their second article, "Electrical analogues of variable profile beams", the same authors describe how to obtain circuits analogous to bent variable profile beams using the four terminal network representation of a vibrating rod.

The article by A. M. Il'evskii, "Physical and mathematical analogues in constructional problems", deals with analogues of thermally treated concrete parts.

In his paper, "On the electrical analogue of a bent rod used by Corbett and Calvert", G. Ye. Pukhov analyses electrical analogues of a bent rod first used by the American scientists Corbett and Calvert.

All the results published in this volume were tested by the authors experimentally and proved satisfactory.

The electrical analogues described can assist those involved in the research and practice of structural mechanics, and are equally interesting to scientists working in computing laboratories.

STATIC SOLUTION OF A TWISTED THIN-WALLED ROD UNDER LOAD USING AN ELECTRICAL ANALOGUE*

K.K. KEROPYAN

METHODS of electrical analogues have recently been applied to the solutions of various problems of building mechanics. Specially rapid development was made following the published work of Prof. Pukhov [1]† in 1952 in which the complex eight terminal network and the simple three terminal active network analogue of a bent rod are described. A short time after, a number of research workers [1, 2, 5] used this system for solving many present-day problems of statics, and dynamics of elastic systems.

But a number of problems of the resistances of materials still wait to be solved using electrical analogues, for instance, torsion of thin-walled rods of both open and closed profile.

The following article shows that many problems concerning the resistances of materials can be solved using electrical analogues, namely the three terminal active network used by Prof. Pukhov for bent rods.

---

* *Presented 9th April 1957 at the united session of the resistance of materials section and the constructional mechanics section of the Rostov-on-Don Civil Engineering Institute.*

† *Here and elsewhere in this publication, the figure in square brackets refers to the numbered source of references at the end of each article.*

K.K. *Keropyan*

Application of the Active 'T' Network Electrical Analogue of a Twisting Thin-walled Rod of Open Profile

We shall analyse (see Fig. 1) a pin-jointed rod of open profile at the ends of which act bending-torsion bi-moments and in the span of which act a concentrated torque L_i, a concentrated bi-moment L_{Mi} and an equally distributed load of m_i kg/cm intensity.

It is known, from the theory of torsion, that the derivatives of the angles of twist at the rod supports are determined [4] by the formulae:

$$\left.\begin{aligned}
\theta_n^{(l)} &= \frac{B_{n-1}l_n}{EJ_{\omega,\,n}}\,r_n + \frac{B_n l_n}{EJ_{\omega,\,n}}\,s_n + \theta_{n,\,p}^{\,\prime(l)}; \\
-\theta_n^{\prime(r)} &= \frac{B_{n-1}l_n}{EJ_{\omega,\,n}}\,s_n + \frac{B_n l_n}{EJ_{\omega,\,n}}\,r_n - \theta_{n,\,p}^{\,\prime(r)},
\end{aligned}\right\} \tag{1}$$

where r_n and s_n are functions of the parameter $u = k_n l_n$: where $k_n = \sqrt{\left(\dfrac{GJ_{k,\,n}}{EJ_{\omega,\,n}}\right)}$ the elastic bending-torsion constant. The functions r_n and s_n are determined [4] from formulae

$$\left.\begin{aligned}
r_n &= \frac{u_n \cos u_n - \sin u_n}{u_n^2 \sin u_n}; \\
s_n &= \frac{\sin u_n - u_n}{u_n^2 \sin u_n},
\end{aligned}\right\} \tag{2}$$

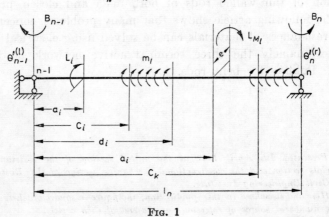

Fig. 1

2

$\theta_{n,p}^{'(1)}$ $\theta_{n,p}^{'(r)}$ are the derivatives of the angles of twist on the left and right supports of the bar, from the span load (which must necessarily be predetermined) respectively. The formula of bi-moments is convenient for this purpose in its initial parameters as shown by S.Ya. Sadetov in his work "Bi-moments formula in initial parameters" (see following paper). This formula is:

$$B_k = B_0 \cos k_n x + \frac{M_\omega^0}{k_n} \sin kx + \sum_{i=1}^{k-1} \frac{L_i}{k_n} \sin k_n(x-a_i) +$$

$$+ \sum_{i=1}^{k-1} \frac{m_k}{k_n^2} [\cos k_n(x-c_i) - \cos k_n(x-d_i)] +$$

$$+ \frac{m_k}{k_n^2} [\cos k_n(x-c_k) - 1] - \sum_{i=1}^{k-1} L_{M_i} \cos k_n(x-a_i). \qquad (3)$$

Here B_0 — bi-moment at the beginning of the coordinates;

L_i — concentrated torque;

m_k — intensity of the distributed momentary load;

L_{Mi} — concentrated bi-moment;

x — abscissa for the analysed section;

a_i — abscissa of the point i, the point of application of L_i. Bearing in mind that

$$M_\omega^0 = L_n^{(1)} - GJ_{k,n}\theta_{n,p}^{'(1)}, \qquad (4)$$

where M_ω^0 — bending torsion moment at the beginning of the coordinates from the span load;

$L_n^{(1)}$ — torque at the beginning of the coordinates of a span, that is support of the nth span;

$GJ_{k,n}$ — rigidity of bars of non-circular profile during torsion.

We shall find $\theta_{n,p}^{(1)}$ using the following limit conditions.

When $x=0$, $B_k=B_0=0$ (free distortion of the plane) and when $x=l$, $B_k=0$.

3

K.K. Keropyan

Fulfilling these conditions and after simple transformations we get:

$$\left.\begin{array}{l} \theta_{n,\,p}^{'(\mathrm{l})} = \dfrac{L_n^{(\mathrm{l})}\sinh u_n + k_n\Phi_n^{(\mathrm{l})}}{GJ_{k,\,n}\sinh u_n}; \\[3mm] \theta_{n,\,p}^{'(\mathrm{r})} = \dfrac{L_n^{(\mathrm{r})}\sinh u_n - k_n\Phi_{,}^{(\mathrm{r})}}{GJ_{k,\,n}\sinh u_n}, \end{array}\right\} \tag{5}$$

where $L_n^{(\mathrm{l})}$, $L_n^{(\mathrm{r})}$ — torque on the supports to the left and right of the span load respectively.

$$\Phi_n^{(\mathrm{l})} = \sum_{i=1}^{k-1} \frac{L_i}{k_n}\sinh k_n(l_n - a_i) + \sum_{i=1}^{k-1} \frac{m_i}{k_n^2}\left[\cosh k_n(l_n - c_i) - \right.$$
$$\left. - \cosh k_n(l_n - d_i)\right] + \frac{m_k}{k_n^2}\left[\cosh k_n(l_n - c_k) - 1\right] -$$
$$- \sum_{i=1}^{k-1} L_{M_i}\cosh k_n(l_n - a_i). \tag{6}$$

$$\Phi_n^{(\mathrm{r})} = \sum_{i=1}^{k-1} \frac{L_i}{k_n}\sinh k_n a_i + \sum_{i=1}^{k-1} \frac{m_i}{k_n^2}\left[\cosh k_n d_i - \cosh k_n c_i\right] +$$
$$+ \frac{m_k}{k_n^2}\left[\cosh k_n l_n - \cosh k_n c_k\right] - \sum_{i=1}^{k-1} L_{M_i}\cosh k_n a_i. \tag{7}$$

The three terminal active network ('T' network) analogue of a thin-walled bar (Fig. 1) is shown in Fig. 2.

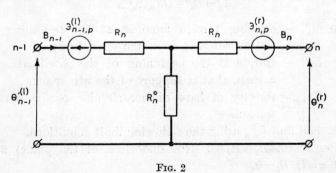

FIG. 2

4

The differentials of the angles of twist are represented by e.m.fs and the bi-moments by currents in the electrical network. Mesh analysis of the network gives the following equations:

$$\left.\begin{aligned}
\theta_n^{'(l)} &= B_{n-1}(R_n + R_n^0) - B_n R_n^0 + \ni_{n,p}^{(l)}; \\
\theta_n^{'(r)} &= B_{n-1}R_n^0 - B_n(R_n + R_n^0) + \ni_{n,p}^{(r)}.
\end{aligned}\right\} \tag{8}$$

Taking the following values for the parameters of the network:

$$\left.\begin{aligned}
R_n &= \frac{r_n + s_n}{EJ_{\omega,n}} l_n; \\
R_n^0 &= -\frac{s_n}{EJ_{\omega,n}} l_n;
\end{aligned}\right\} \tag{9}$$

$$\left.\begin{aligned}
\ni_{n,p}^{(l)} &= \theta_{n,p}^{'(l)}; \\
\ni_{n,p}^{(r)} &= \theta_{n,p}^{'(r)},
\end{aligned}\right\} \tag{10}$$

equations (8) and (1) become identical.

Calculation for Solid Beams

Beams of a thin-walled profile with an open cross section in constrained torsion can be calculated with the help of the equation of three bi-moments. We shall analyse two adjoining spans of a solid beam (Fig. 3a) which has different rigidities in the various segments. The equation of three bi-moments according to [4] takes the form:

$$B_{n-1}\frac{l_n}{J_{\omega,n}} s_n + B_n\left(\frac{l_n}{J_{\omega,n}} r_n + \frac{l_{n+1}}{J_{\omega,n+1}} r_{n+1}\right) +$$

$$+ B_{n+1}\frac{l_{n+1}}{J_{\omega,n+1}} s_{n+1} = E[\theta_{n,p}^{'(r)} - \theta_{n+1,p}^{'(l)}], \tag{11}$$

where r_n and s_n are functions of the parameter u, determined from formulae (2).

The electrical network analogue of the beam is shown in Fig. 3b.

5

The equation for the nth mesh is

$$(B_n - B_{n-1})R_n^0 + B_n(R_n + R_{n+1}) + (B_n - B_{n+1})R_{n+1}^0 = \mathbf{\ni}_{n, p}^{(r)} - \mathbf{\ni}_{n+1, p}^{(l)},$$

giving

$$-B_{n-1}R_n^0 + B_n(R_n + R_n^0 + R_{n+1} + R_{n+1}^0) - B_{n+1}R_{n+1}^0 = \mathbf{\ni}_{n, p}^{(r)} - \mathbf{\ni}_{n, p}^{(l)}. \tag{12}$$

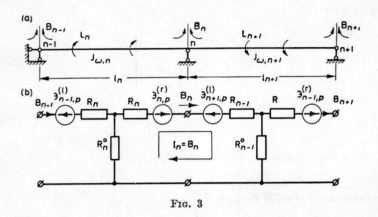

FIG. 3

Substituting the following expressions (13) and (14) for the network parameters in equation (12), gives an identical expression to equation (11).

$$
\left.
\begin{aligned}
R_n^0 &= -\frac{s_n l_n}{E J_{\omega,n}}; \\
R_n &= \frac{(s_n + r_n)l_n}{E J_{\omega,n}}; \\
R_{n+1}^0 &= -\frac{s_{n+1} l_{n+1}}{E J_{\omega,n+1}}; \\
R_{n+1} &= \frac{(s_{n+1} + r_{n+1})l_{n+1}}{E J_{\omega,n+1}}.
\end{aligned}
\right\} \tag{13}
$$

$$
\left.
\begin{aligned}
\mathbf{\ni}_{n, p}^{(r)} &= \theta_{n, p}^{\prime\,(r)}; \\
\mathbf{\ni}_{n+1, p}^{(l)} &= \theta_{n+1, p}^{\prime\,(l)}.
\end{aligned}
\right\} \tag{14}
$$

6

Constrained Torsion of a Thin-walled Bar of a Closed Profile

When calculating profiles of a closed shape, the operations used in calculating open profiles of beams with arbitrary supports are repeated. The procedure is the same in the case of a solid beam [4]. Therefore functions of influences and initial differential equations are also valid for closed profiles. The differences between calculating open or closed profile beams, according to [4], are:

(1) The torsion-flexure constant is calculated from the formula:

$$k = \sqrt{\left(\frac{GJ_{k,n}}{EJ_{\omega,n}} \mu \right)} \tag{15}$$

where μ is a coefficient of the plane section distortion.

(2) The method of obtaining sectional characteristics is different in the two cases.

(3) Formulae for the determination of tangential tensions in closed profiles contain additional constant members which are not present in the formulae for open profiles.

These differences do not change the character of the problem. As long as the structure of the basic equations (1) remain unchanged the three terminal active network may also be used as the analogue, for constrained torsion calculations, of a rod with a closed profile.

Practical Experiment

To calculate some problems of building mechanics and resistances of materials, the laboratory of computing machines of the Taganrog Radiotechnical Institute constructed the computing electrical analogue* EMSS-1. A three terminal active network is the basis of this machine. Below we shall see the results

* Description of the analogue EMSS-1 is given in the article by O.V. Il'enko and V. I. Usynin in this collection of articles.

of solving some problems of hampered torsion with the help of this analogue.

EXAMPLE. We have a tree-span solid beam with equal spans $l=4$m, loaded at the centre of the two end spans with a concentrated torque $M_{kp}=20,000$ kg/cm. The middle span is loaded along its whole length with a distributed load of intensity $m=100$ kg/cm.

We have to find the bi-moments B_2, B_3 on the intermediary rests. The profile of the beam — I-beam No. 20; $k=0.0207$ cm^{-1};

$$J_\omega = 13,121 \text{ cm}^6; \quad E=2\times10^6 \text{ kg/cm}^2.$$

Solution. According to tables [4] the values of the functions r_n and s_n if ($l=0.0207\times400=8.28$); are $r_1=r_2=r_3=0.1$; $s_1=s_2=s_3=0.014$. From formulae 5 the derivatives of the angles of twist at the span loads:

$$\theta_1'^{(l)} = \theta_3'^{(l)} = 0.26\times10^{-3}; \quad \theta_2'^{(l)} = 0.4\times10^{-3};$$

$$\theta_1'^{(r)} = \theta_3'^{(r)} = -0.26\times10^{-3}; \quad \theta_2'^{(r)} = -0.4\times10^{-3}.$$

Using the equation of three bi-moments (11) we get:

$$B_2 = B_3 = -202,000 \text{ kg/cm}^2.$$

According to formulae (13) and (14) we substitute the following values for the parameters of the electrical circuit

$$R_1 = R_2 = R_3 = \frac{0.1+0.014}{2\times10^6\times13,121}\ 400 = 174\times10^{-11};$$

$$R_1^0 = R_2^0 = R_3^0 = -\frac{0.014\times400}{2\times10^6\times13,121} = -21.3\times10^{-11};$$

$$\ni_1^{(l)} = \ni_3^{(l)} = 0.26\times10^{-3}; \quad \ni_2^{(l)} = 0.4\times10^{-3};$$

$$\ni_1^{(r)} = \ni_3^{(r)} = -0.26\times10^{-3}; \quad \ni_2^{(r)} = -0.4\times10^{-3}.$$

If we take the following scales, for resistances m_R and e.m.f $m_\ni$:

$$m_R = 5.00\times10^{11}; \quad m_\ni = 0.77\times10^5,$$

and this for currents:

$$m_B = \frac{m_\ni}{m_R} = \frac{0.77\times10^5}{5.00\times10^{11}} = 0.154\times10^{-6}.$$

The final parameters the three terminal network thus become

$$\hat{R}_1 = \hat{R}_2 = \hat{R}_3 = m_R R_1 = 5.00\times10^{11}\times174\times10^{-11} = 870\ \Omega;$$

$$\hat{R}_1^0 = \hat{R}_2^0 = \hat{R}_3^0 = m_R R_1^0 = -5.00\times10^{11}\times21.3\times10^{-11} = -107\ \Omega;$$

8

$$\hat{\Im}_1^{1(l)} = \hat{\Im}_3^{1(l)} = m_\Im \; \Im_3^{(l)} = 0.77 \times 10^5 \times 0.26 \times 10^{-3} = -20V;$$

$$\hat{\Im}_1^{1(r)} = \hat{\Im}_3^{1(r)} = m_\Im \; \Im_3^{(r)} = -0.77 \times 10^5 \times 0.26 \times 10^{-3} = -20V;$$

$$\hat{\Im}_2^{1(l)} = \hat{\Im}_2^{1(l)} \; m_\Im = 0.4 \times 10^{-3} \times 0.77 \times 10^5 = 31V;$$

$$\hat{\Im}_2^{1(r)} = \hat{\Im}_2^{1(r)} \; m_\Im = -0.4 \times 10^{-3} \times 0.77 \times 10^5 = -31V.$$

We shall determine the magnitude of the scale coefficient:

$$k_x = \frac{1}{r_x m_B} = \frac{1}{870 \times 0.154 \times 10^{-6}} = 7500,$$

in the given case $r_x = R_1$:

We shall use the three terminal network of Pukhov and Il'enko and measure the terminal voltages

$$E = -25.4V.$$

Bi-moment $B_2 = k_x E = 25.4 \times 7500 = -190500 \; kg/cm^2$.
Thus the error is

$$\delta = \frac{202,00 - 190,500}{202,000} = 5.7\%.$$

Conclusions

From the above example it follows that the three terminal active network given by Prof. Pukhov and Il'enko originally for bending bars can also be used for calculations of bending and torsion of thin-walled bars of open and closed profiles. This can be done on the electrical analogue EMSS-1.

References

1. G.YE. PUKHOV, *On the question of applying methods of electrical analogues to problems of bending plane beam systems*. Publishing House of the Tomsk Polytechnical Institute. 72. Tomsk 1952.
2. P.M. CHEGOLIN, Comparison of methods of constructional dynamics with the theory of calculating electrical circuits. (Page 77, this volume).
3. S.YA. SADETOV, Bi-moments formula of initial parameters (Page 10, this volume).
4. I.V. URBAN, *Design theory of thin-walled rod constructions*. Transzheldorizdat 1955.
5. O.V. IL'ENKO and V.I. USYNIN, Electrical analogue EMSS-1 designed for calculating beams and frameworks. (Page 42, this volume).

BI-MOMENTS FORMULA
IN INITIAL PARAMETERS*

S.YA. SADETOV

RESEARCH, being developed in the Rostov-on-Don Civil Engineering Institute and Taganrog Radiotechnical Institute, in the
field of electrical analogues used in building mechanics, covers
more and more practical questions of technical calculations in
connection with determining stresses and deformations in building constructions.†

One of the most tedious problems in practice is the determining of forces occurring in constrained torsion of thin-walled bars:
in particular the flexure-torsion bi-moment B, flexure-torsion
moment M_ω and moment of plain torsion M_k. Calculations of
these magnitudes is usually done by way of differential equations
of constrained torsion which takes the form:

$$\theta^{IV} - k^2\theta'' = -\frac{m}{EJ_\omega}, \tag{1}$$

where

θ — angle of twist of the bar;

k — flexure-torsion constant;

m — intensity of the disturbed twisting force;

E — modulus of elasticity;

J_ω — moment of inertia of the bar's section.

---

* Presented at the joint session of the resistance of materials section and
constructional mechanics section of RISI 1st November 1956.
† See preceding article in this collection.

In cases, where the bar is loaded only with concentrated torques and the distributed torsion is absent, the equation (1) is transformed into the homogeneous equation:

$$\theta^{\mathrm{IV}} - k^2\theta'' = 0. \tag{2}$$

Solutions of equations (1) and (2) are usually given in initial parameters and contain four initial parameters (constants of integration). The solution in such a form is not convenient for application to electrical analogues as the determination of the necessary parameters for the electrical model is very difficult. In place of equation (2) it is possible to use the differential equation of bi-moments in order to determine the forces in torsion. This, when the distributed torsion force is absent, takes the form:

$$B'' - k^2 B = 0. \tag{3}$$

Solution of this equation is usually expressed in hyperbolic, functions and is of the form:

$$B = C_1 \cosh kx + C_2 \sinh kx. \tag{4}$$

However, this method of calculation is convenient neither for electrical analogues nor for calculating the various forces on the beam.

In the following article a formula for calculating bi-moments is given. It is based on the use of initial parameters for the integration of a differential equation (3).

Professor K.K. Keropyan, in an article included in this book, successfully used this formula in order to determine parameters of the electrical analogue.

We must point out that the formula mentioned below enormously simplifies calculating work on bi-moments.

Derivation of the Formula of Bi-moments

We shall analyse a bar (Fig. 1) of an arbitrary length, loaded with concentrated torques L, torques distributed on separate sections of intensity m and flexture moments M, the plane of action of which is at a distance e from the centre line of the bar. We shall denote the symbols for force factors at the beginning of the coordinates as B_0, M_ω^0 and M_e^0. We shall calculate the general meaning of bi-moments on the basis of independence of the action of forces.

(a) *Influence of concentrated torques*

We shall determine the value of bi-moment on the segment of the bar (shown in Fig. 1), where torque L_1 is applied in a section of distance x from the beginning of the coordinates.

From formula (4) we can write:

$$B_1 = C_1 \cosh kx + C_2 \sinh kx. \tag{5}$$

At the beginning of coordinants $x=0$, thus we have $B_1 = B_0$; substituting these values into formula (5), we obtain $C_1 = B_0$. Differentiating equation (5) and remembering that

$$\frac{dB}{dx} = M_\omega, \text{ we get:}$$

$$M_\omega = kC_1 \sinh kx + kC_2 \cosh kx$$

when $x=0$, $M_\omega = M_\omega^0$: thus $C_2 = \dfrac{M_\omega^0}{k}$.

Thus formula (5) takes the following form:

$$B_1 = B_0 \cosh kx + \frac{M_\omega^0}{k} \sinh kx.$$

We shall determine the value of bi-moment on the section of the bar between the torques L_1 and L_2. Differential equation (3) for this section will be:

$$B_2'' - k^2 B_2 = 0. \tag{6}$$

We shall denote the increase on this segment as a function of $(x - a_1)$, that is:

$$\Delta B = B_2 - B_1 = \varphi(x - a_1);$$

12

giving

$$B_2 = B_1 + \varphi(x - a_1)$$

substituting in equation (6) for B_2 and B_2'', we obtain:

$$B' + \varphi''(x - a_1) - k^2 B_1 - k^2 \varphi(x - a_1) = 0.$$

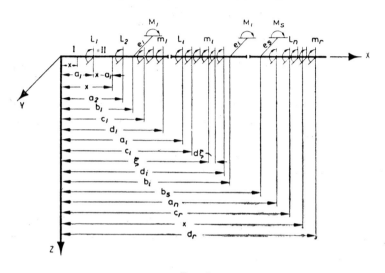

FIG. 1

From equation (3) we know $B_1'' - k^2 B_1 = 0$
therefore:

$$\varphi''(x - a_1) - k^2 \varphi(x - a_1) = 0.$$

The solution of this equation can be expressed in the form:

$$\varphi(x - a_1) = C_3 \cosh k(x - a_1) + C_4 \sinh k(x - a_1). \tag{7}$$

When $x = a_1$, the value of the bi-moment on this segment of the bar is equal to the value of the bi-moment of the preceding segment as the bi-moment is a function of the corresponding longitudinal elongations of the bar and with $x = a_1$ the lengths on both segments are equal. Consequently when $x = a_1$

$$\varphi(x - a_1) = \Delta B = 0 \text{ and therefore } C_3 = 0.$$

13

Differentiating (7) and using $\varphi'(x-a_1)=(\Delta B)'=\Delta M_\omega$ and also including the value obtained for C_3, we obtain:

$$\Delta M_\omega = kC_4 \cosh k(x-a_1);$$

from which, when

$$x=a_1 \text{ we have } C_4 = \frac{\Delta M_\omega}{k}$$

and equation (7) becomes

$$\varphi(x-a_1) = \frac{\Delta M_\omega}{k} \sinh k(x-a_1). \tag{8}$$

From the theory of calculation of thin-walled bars, worked out by Prof. V.Z. Vlasov [1], it is known that $M_\omega = L - M_k$ and consequently:

$$\Delta M_\omega = \Delta L - \Delta M_k.$$

Also we know that $M_k = GJ_k\theta'$ and therefore

$$\Delta M_k = GJ_k\theta'.$$

We shall analyse the plane deformation of the section when $x=a_1$. The magnitude of the plane deformation is expressed on the formula

$$u = -\omega\theta'.$$

For the first segment of the bar we can write $u_1 = -\omega\theta'$, and for the second segment

$$u_2 = -\omega(\theta' + \Delta\theta').$$

We shall analyse the section when $x=a_1$: in this case the plane deformations of the first and second segments are equal, that is $u_1 = u_2$ from where, with a transition beyond this section, we have $\Delta\theta' = 0$, and consequently:

$$\Delta M_k = 0; \quad \Delta M_\omega = \Delta L = L_1$$

$$\text{and } C_4 = \frac{L_1}{k}.$$

As a result of this analysis we must stress that the application of a concentrated torque does not cause a jumping change of

14

the clear torsion moment but causes a jumping change of the flexure-torsion moment only. Thus, the increase of bi-moment under the transition from one segment to another is expressed in the following formula

$$\varphi(x-a_1) = \Delta B = \frac{L_1}{k} \sinh k(x-a_1), \tag{9}$$

and the magnitude of bi-moment on the second segment of the bar equals:

$$B_2 = B_0 \cosh kx + \frac{M_\omega^0}{k} \sinh kx + \frac{L_1}{k} \sinh k(x-a_1).$$

Repeating the same argument we shall obtain for the n-segment of the bar the following equation:

$$B_n = B_0 \cosh kx + \frac{M_\omega^0}{k} \sinh kx + \sum_{i=1}^{n-1} \frac{L_i}{k} \sinh k(x-a_i). \tag{10}$$

(b) *The influence of a distributed torsion load*

In order to preserve formula (3) we single out on the ith segment an infinitely small section $d\xi$ in the distance ξ from the beginning of the coordinates containing a momentary distributed force m_i (Fig. 1). The influence of load on this small section, on the value of bi-moment, can be determined from the influence of the infinitely small concentrated torque $dL_i = m_i d\xi$. Then according to formula (9) the increase of bi-moment on the whole ith segment with the distributed momentary load will be:

$$\Delta B_{m_i} = \int_{c_i}^{d_i} \frac{m_i d\xi}{k} \sinh k(x-\xi).$$

The increase in bi-moment for the rth section with a distributed momentary load (Fig. 1) is expressed in the formula

$$\Delta B_{m_i} = \sum_{=1}^{r-1} \int_{c_i}^{d_i} \frac{m_i}{k} \sinh k(x-\xi) d\xi + \int_c^x \frac{m_r}{k} \sinh k(x-\xi) d\xi. \tag{11}$$

15

If the distributed momentary load at the end of every segment is constant then after integration formula (11) takes the form:

$$\Delta B_{m_i} = \sum_{i=1}^{r-1} \frac{m_i}{k^2} \left[\cosh k(x-c_i) - \cosh k(x-d_i) \right] +$$

$$+ \frac{m_r}{k^2} [\cosh k(x-c_r) - 1]. \tag{12}$$

(c) *The influence of concentrated bending moments*

In accordance with Prof. Vlasov's way of determining the magnitude of bi-moments, created by the bending moment, it is necessary to find an expression for the bending moment at a distance e from the plane of its action at the centre line of bending of the bar; then we shall substitute the expression Me into the formula of bi-moments for the concentrated torque and take a partial derivative of this expression in the distance from the beginning of the coordinates to the point of application of the bending moment.

Using formula (9) and the expressions in Fig. 1. we shall obtain the magnitude of the increase of bi-moment due to the action of a concentrated bending moment M_1 in the form of:

$$\Delta B_{M1} = \frac{\partial}{\partial b} \left[\frac{1}{k} M_1 e_1 \sinh k(x-b_1) \right] = - M_1 e_1 \cosh k(x-b_1).$$

The increase of bi-moment due to the action of concentrated bending moments is equal to:

$$\Delta B_M = - \sum_{i=1}^{s} M_i e_i \cosh k(x-b_i). \tag{13}$$

Using formulae (10), (12) and (13) we get a recurrence formula of bi-moments due to forces shown in Fig. 1 for the end right-hand section:

$$B_n = B_0 \cosh kx + \frac{M_\omega^0}{k} \sinh kx + \sum_{i=1}^{n-1} \frac{L_i}{k} \sinh k(x-a_i) +$$

16

$$+ \sum_{i=1}^{x-1} {}' \frac{m_i}{k^2} \left[\cosh k(x-c_i) - \cosh k(x-d_i) \right] +$$

$$+ \frac{m_r}{k^2} \left[\cosh k(x-c_r) - 1 \right] - \sum_{i=1} {}' M_i e_i \cosh k(x-b_i). \quad (14)$$

Determination of Initial Parameters

In the recurrence formula (14) we have two initial parameters V_0 and M_ω^0 which must be determined according to the fastenings of the supports of the bar. From the theory [1] of calculating thin-walled bars we know that in sections, where distortion of the plane is not possible, the moment of torsion $M_k = 0$. This means that the flexure-torsion moment in these sections is equal to the outer torque, that is $M_\omega = L$. Apart from this we know

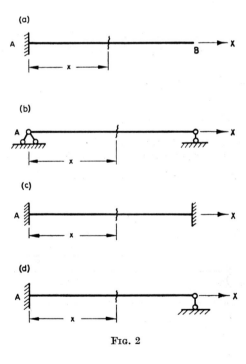

(a)

(b)

(c)

(d)

Fig. 2

17

that in the sections, where the plane distortion has no constraints, the bi-moment equals 0. These criteria therefore determine the first initial parameter from the conditions of fastening the left end of the bar and the second initial parameter from the conditions of fastening the right-hand end of the bar. We shall consider the initial parameters for the beams shown (Fig. 2).

A beam fixed at one end (Fig. 2a):

when $x = 0$ we have $M_k^0 = 0$ and $M_\omega^0 = L_a$ (torque at the support);

when $x = l$ we have $B = 0$;

from here we can determine B_0.

A beam freely placed on two supports (Fig. 2b):

when $x = 0$ we have $B = 0$ and $B_0 = 0$;

when $x = l$ we have $B = 0$;

from here we can determine M_ω^0.

A beam fixed at two ends (Fig. 2c):

when $x = 0$ we have $M_k^0 = 0$ and $M_\omega^0 = L_a$;

when $x = l$ we have $M_\omega = l_b$;

from here after differentiating formula (14) we can determine B_0.

A beam fixed at one end and pin-jointed at the other (Fig. 2d):

when $x = 0$ we have $M_\omega^0 = L_a$;

when $x = l$ we have $B = 0$;

from here we can determine B_0.

EXAMPLE. To determine the forces of torsion with constraints in the beam shown in Fig. 3. The data given are: $P = 50$ kg; $q = 0 \cdot 3$ kg/cm; $M = 200$ kg/cm; the flexure-torsion characteristic of the cross section of the beam $k = 0 \cdot 00881 \dfrac{1}{\text{cm}}$ $e = 5$ cm.

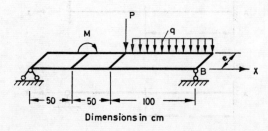

Dimensions in cm

FIG. 3

Bi-moments Formula in Initial Parameters

Solution. On the basis of the importance of initial parameters we shall conclude that bi-moment at the beginning of the coordinates $B_0 = B$; in order to determine the second initial parameter we take formula (14) for the segment of the beam joined to the right-hand end and taking the bi-moment as equal to 0 and x equal to l we obtain:

$$0 = \frac{M_\omega^0}{k} \sinh kl + \frac{L_1}{k} \sinh k(x-100) + \frac{m}{k^2}[\cosh k(x-100)-1] - $$
$$- Me \cosh k(x-50).$$

From here we find the magnitude of the flexure-torsion at the beginning of coordinates:

$$M_\omega^0 = -\frac{1}{\sinh kl}\left\{ L \sinh k(l-100) + \frac{m}{k}[\cosh k(l-100)-1] - \right.$$
$$\left. - kMe \cosh k(l-50) \right\}.$$

Using the given data we get:

$$\sinh kl = \sinh (0.00881 \times 200) = 2.82;$$
$$\sinh k(l-100) = \sinh 0.881 = 0.999;$$
$$\cosh k(l-100) = \cosh 0.881 = 1.41$$
$$L = Pe = 50 \times 5 = 250 \text{ kg/cm};$$
$$m = qe = 0.3 \times 5 = 1.5 \text{ kgcm/cm};$$
$$Me = 200 \times 5 = 1000 \text{ kgcm}^2;$$

$$M_\omega^0 = -\frac{1}{2.82}\left[250 \times 0.999 + \frac{1.5}{0.00881}(1.41-1) - 0.00881 \times 1000 \times 2.007 \right] =$$
$$= -107 \text{ kgcm}.$$

According to formula (14) we take the forces on the separate segments of the beams:
1st segment $0 \le x \le 50$:

$$B_1 = \frac{M_\omega^0}{k} \sinh kx;$$

$$M_{\omega_1} = -M_\omega^0 \cosh kx;$$

$$M_{k_1} = L_A - M_\omega, \text{ where } L_A = 0.5L + \frac{1}{8} ml.$$

2nd segment $50 < x \le 100$:

$$B_2 = -\frac{M_\omega^0}{k} \sinh kx - Me \cosh k(x-50);$$

$$M_{\omega_2} = -M_\omega^0 \cosh kx - kMe \sinh k(x-50);$$

$$M_{k_2} = L_A - M_{\omega_2}.$$

19

3rd segment $100 \leq x \leq 200$:

$$B_3 = -\frac{M_\omega^0}{k} \sinh kx - Me \cosh k(x-50) + \frac{L}{k} \sinh k(x-100) +$$

$$+ \frac{m}{k} \sinh k(x-100);$$

$$M_{\omega_3} = -M_\omega^0 \cosh kx - kMe \sinh k(x-50) + L \cosh k(x-100) +$$

$$+ \frac{m}{k} \sinh k(x-100);$$

$$M_{k_3} = L_A - L - M_{\omega_3}.$$

The largest bi-moment will be in the section where the flexure-torsion moment equals 0 which takes place when $x = 100$ cm; here M_ω changes sign.
Then

$$B_{max} = -\frac{M_\omega^0}{k} \sinh 100k - Me \cosh 50k = -\frac{107}{0.0081} \times 0.999 - 1000 \times 1.098 =$$

$$= -13,250 \text{ kgcm}^2.$$

Reference

1. V.Z. VLASOV, *Thin-walled elastic beams.* Stroiizdat 1940.

3

ELECTRICAL ANALOGUES
OF SOME PLANE ROD SYSTEMS*

K.K. KEROPYAN

IT IS a well known fact that many problems of building mechanics (e.g. calculations of horizontal spacial frames, statically indeterminate beams, curves of influences, deformations) require tedious work for their solution and often take considerable time as they are connected with long and difficult calculations even in comparatively simple plans of buildings, not to speak of multi-storied frames and other more complex constructions.

Numerous existing methods of approximation for calculating complex problems of building mechanics are comparatively uneconomical.

Recently, many attempts have been made to solve such problems using electrical analogues.

From the material published during recent years in this field, the most interesting, in my opinion, are the works of Prof. G.Ye. Pukhov [1] and his pupils P.M. Chegolin [2] and O.V. Il'enko [3]. Professor G.Ye. Pukhov's work shows that the problem of bending horizontal rod systems is analogous to an active electrical 'T' network; this enables us to construct analogues of horizontal frames very easily, and with their help to determine the moments, and angles of deflection.

The electrical scheme suggested by Pukhov, as the analogue

---

* Presented at the joint session of the resistance of materials section and the constructional mechanics section of RISI 1st November, 1956.

of a bending rod, has two sources of e.m.f., their magnitude being determined as follows:

$$\ni_1 = \frac{\omega v}{EJ}; \tag{1}$$

$$\ni_2 = \frac{\omega u}{EJ}, \tag{2}$$

where ω — the area of the curve of bending moment of the rod;

u and v — the coordinates of the gravitational centre of the curve of bending moment with regard to the rod supports.

EJ — rigidity of the rod.

Translated into the language of building mechanics, the e.m.f.'s $\ni_1$ and $\ni_2$ represent the angles of deflection of the bending rod's profile.

This way, in order to use the analogue of G.Ye. Pukhov and O.V. Il'enko for solving the problem of bending rods, it is necessary to calculate the magnitudes of $\ni_1$ and $\ni_2$ for every rod. Even in comparatively simple methods of supporting the bending rod, the determination of the momentary plane requires long and tedious work in calculating determinate integrals. It is therefore natural that attempts have been made to perform even this part of the work on the analogue.

The research made by the above mentioned authors showed that it is possible to construct an electrical analogue of a bending rod by making use of some similarities existing between the theory of electrical design of lines with duplex feed and the theory known in building mechanics as the grapho-analytic method for the determination of deformations.

On this analogue it is possible to determine bending moments, intersecting forces, deflections and angles of turn for arbitrary profiles of the analysed rod, including their supports. The latter must be known when calculating frames on the analogue of G.Ye. Pukhov and O.V. Il'enko. Later on we shall describe the

22

scheme and results of analysing an electrical analogue of a bending rod acted on by an arbitrary transverse load.

After this analogue was constructed and analysed, the work of C.W. Riesz and B.I. Swain appeared on the same subject. These two authors work on the similarities between the potential energy of bending and the electrical energy accumulated in a condenser and they construct their analogue with alternating current. We refer the reader to the original works and will concentrate only on the similarity and difference of these two analogues of a bending rod.

When solving statically indeterminate problems on our analogue we compare deformations, whereas the analogue of C.W. Riesz and B.I. Swain compares the energies involved (Catiliano theorem). The principles of designing electrical curves to represent bending moments and the intersecting forces for simple beams are the same. But the problem of deformation in a girder is not posed in [7] and would be quite impossible to solve on their analogue. Also the determination of the signs of the required magnitudes is much more simple on an analogue using direct current. Again the accuracy of measuring e.m.f. and currents in the analogue is higher when using d.c. analogues than when using a.c.

We shall analyse the electrical analogue of a beam placed freely on two supports and arbitrarily loaded.

Theoretical Basis of the Analogue

We shall take a simple beam of constant rigidity loaded with several concentrated forces and moments influencing the supports (Fig. 1). Applying the laws of statics and the graphoanalytic method of determining the deformation of the beam we write the following equations:

$$A = \frac{\Sigma P_i l_{iB}}{l} + \frac{M_B - M_A}{l}; \tag{3}$$

$$B = \frac{\Sigma P_i l_{iA}}{l} - \frac{M_B - M_A}{l}; \qquad (4)$$

$$M_x = Ax - \sum_1^k P_i(x - l_{iA}); \qquad (5)$$

$$\overline{A} = \frac{\sum_1^n \Phi_i l_{iB}}{l}; \qquad (6)$$

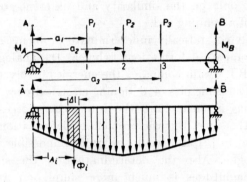

FIG. 1

$$\overline{B} = \frac{\sum_1^n \Phi_i l_{iA}}{l}; \qquad (7)$$

$$\overline{M} = \overline{A}x - \sum_1^k \Phi_i(x - l_{iA}). \qquad (8)$$

Here l_{iB} — arm of the force Φ_i from the support B.

According to the formulae (3)–(8) the problem of bending of a freely placed beam is fully solved. We shall show that there is a complete similarity between the closed electrical circuit with duplex feed and the above mentioned equations. Consider the analysis of the electrical loop shown (Fig. 2). The distribution of the current in the loop does not change if at points A and B we imagine the loop being cut and straightened out into a line (Fig. 2b).

We shall find the distribution of the currents in a closed loop if the resistances of all the parts are known and the potential $U_B > U_A$.

Applying the 2nd law of Kirchhoff to the line AB, we have

$$I_{A1}r_{A1} + (I_{A1} - i_1)r_{12} + (I_{A1} - i_1 - i_2)r_{23} + \ldots +$$

$$+ (I_1 - \sum_1^n i_n)r_{nB} = U_B - U_A. \qquad (9)$$

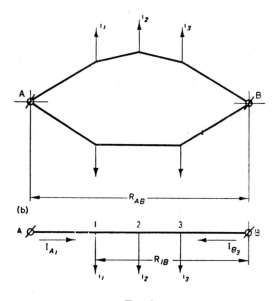

(b)

Fig. 2

The resistance of the reverse lead we shall assume equal to zero. Rearranging the terms, we obtain:

$$I_{A1}(r_{A1} + r_{12} + \ldots + r_{nB}) - i_1(r_{12} + r_{23} + \ldots + r_{nB}) -$$

$$- i_2(r_{23} + r_{34} + \ldots + r_{nB}) - i_n r_{nB} = U_B - U_A.$$

Further:

$$r_{A1} + r_{12} + \ldots + r_{nB} = R_{AB};$$

$$r_{12} + r_{23} + \ldots + r_{nB} = R_{1B};$$

$$\cdot \; \cdot \; \cdot \; \cdot \; \cdot \; \cdot \; \cdot \; \cdot \; \cdot \; \cdot \; \cdot \; \cdot \; \cdot$$

$$r_{nB} = R_{nB}.$$

Finally the magnitudes of the supplied currents are given by

$$I_{A1} = \frac{\sum_{1}^{n} i_i R_{iB}}{R_{AB}} + \frac{U_B - U_A}{R_{AB}} ; \tag{10}$$

$$I_{Bn} = \frac{\sum_{1}^{n} i_i R_{iA}}{R_{AB}} - \frac{U_B - U_A}{R_{AB}}.$$

If we compare formulae (3) and (10) we observe an exact correspondence. This has been noted in earlier technical literature of this country, but as far as we know was utilized for the first time in calculating beams by the authors of this work and the foreign specialists [7], independently of each other.

Now we shall determine the drop in voltage in line AB (Fig. 2), e.g. between points A and 3 (Fig. 2b). Using the second law of Kirchhoff we can write:

$$U_{A3} = I_{A1} r_{A1} + (I_{A1} - i_1) r_{12} + (I_{A1} - i_1 - i_2) r_{23}.$$

Expressing this using the accepted symbols, we obtain:

$$U_{A3} = l_{A1} R_{A3} - i_1 R_{13} - i_2 R_{23}. \tag{11}$$

The equation for the bending moment at point 3 of the beam AB (Fig. 1) takes the following form:

$$M_x = A a_3 - P_1(a_3 - a_1) - P_2(a_3 - a_2). \tag{12}$$

Equations (11) and (12) are identical.

The potential difference between points A and 3 of the cut circle represents to the established scale the bending moment at point 3 of the beam AB (Fig. 1).

The curve of the drop in voltage between points A and B corresponds with the bending moment curve for the beam AB. In conformity with the differential dependance between the bending moment and the transverse force, the currents $i = \frac{\partial U}{\partial R}$, loading the separate sections of the line AB, will to the model scale chosen, represent the transverse forces.

26

On the basis of the above we can imagine a scheme, as in Fig. 3b (circuit AB), of an electrical analogue of the simple beam depicted in Fig. 1.

Developing further this analogy we can also determine the angular and linear deformations of the beam. Following the grapho-analytic method of determining deformation from the resistances of materials, we can analyse the curves of bending

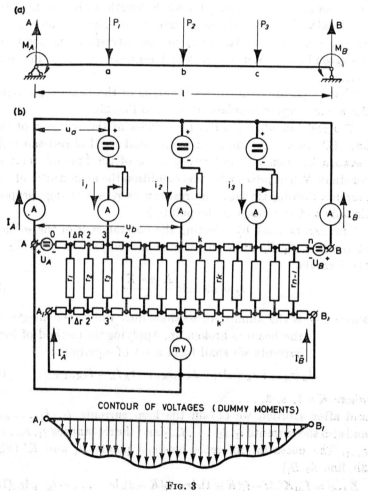

FIG. 3

moments of the actuating load as a load on a fixed beam. By breaking up the plane of the curve M into a number of elementary strips, and by exchanging every one of them for concentrated forces, it is possible with a sufficient degree of accuracy to exchange the continuous load for the concentrated one and thus to bring the problem to the same level as in Fig. 1.

For a hypothetical beam we can similarly design an electrical analogue and feed it along its whole length with currents proportional to the assumed concentrated loads. This can be reached by scanning the resistances r_k in the corresponding points of the given beam, potentials of which represent the bending moments.

The electrical circuit of an analogue of the beam for solving the whole range of problems is given in Fig. 3b.

The resistances r_k and the resistances of the sections of the line AB must match in such a way that the full resistance R_0 between the point A and any point k of the line AB remains constant. When preserving this condition the magnitudes of the currents flowing through the resistances r_k will change proportionally to the voltage at the points k.

This can be done by selecting the resistance Δr of the section of the line $A_1 B_1$ sufficiently small in comparison with R_0 in the formula.

$$r_K = R_0 - \Delta r \frac{K(n-K)}{n}, \qquad (13)$$

where $n-$ is the number of sections into which the length of the beam is broken up. Applying the method of loop currents we shall form a set of equations:

$$I_K(r_{K-1} + r_K + \Delta r) - I_{K-1}r_{K-1} - r_K I_K = E_{(K-1)K}. \qquad (14)$$

where $K = 1, 2, 3, \ldots, n$,
and after solution we obtain the loop currents $I_1, I_2, \ldots, I_n$ and also the currents $i_1, i_2, \ldots, i_{n-1}$ and the resistances $r_1, r_2, \ldots, r_{n-1}$. The potential difference between points A_1 and K' (Fig. 3b, line $A_1 B_1$)

$$E_{A_1 K'} = I_{A_1}K'\Delta r - i_1(K-1)\Delta r - i_2(K-2)\Delta r - \ldots - i_{K-1}\Delta r \qquad (15)$$

28

will give to the given scale the assumed bending moment at the section K' and consequently, also the deflection, as equations (8) and (15) are identical.

We shall determine the scale factor of this analogue. We shall introduce the following symbols:

P — concentrated load on the beam in tons;

l — the span of the beam in metres;

Δl — the length of the section of the beam in metres;

I — current in amps;

U — voltage in volts;

R, r — resistances in ohms of the lines AB and A_1B_1 (Fig. 3);

K_P — scale of forces in tons/amp;

K_l — the scale of lengths in metres/ohm;

$\overline{K_l}$ — the scale of length of the hypothetical beam in metres/ohm;

K_M — the scale of moments in ton metres/volt.

We have:

$$K_P = \frac{P}{I}\,\text{m/A}, \quad K_l = \frac{l}{R}\text{m}/\Omega;$$

$$\overline{K_l} = \frac{l}{r}\,\text{m}/\Omega; \quad K_M = K_P K_l\,\text{mm/V}.$$

Bearing in mind that

$$M_x = U_{AK} K_P K_l;$$

$$\Delta l = \Delta R K_l,$$

where ΔR — is the resistance of the section of the line AB, we shall

find Φ — the assumed load

$$\Phi = M_x \Delta l = U_{AK} \Delta R K_P K_l^2\,\text{mm}^2.$$

The assumed moment

$$\overline{M} = \Phi x_{K'} = U_{AK} \Delta R K_P K_l^2 x_{K'}, \tag{16}$$

$$\text{also} \quad x_{K'} = R_{AK'} \overline{K_l}.$$

We multiply and divide (16) by R_0 – resistance of the load:

$$\overline{M} = \frac{U_{AK}}{R_0} R_0 \Delta R K_P K_i^2 \overline{K}_i R_{AK'}.$$ (17)

As Δr is very small in comparison with r_k (order $1/1000\ r_k$), then with negligible error we can take $r_k \approx R_0$ and then the current, representing the load of the hypothetical beam is:

$$i_\Phi \approx \frac{U_{AK}}{R_0}.$$ (18)

Substituting (18) into (17) and bearing in mind that

$$i_\Phi R_{AK'} = U_{AK'},$$

we shall obtain

$$\overline{M} = U_{AK'} \cdot \varphi R_0 \Delta R K_P K_i^2 \overline{K}_l = U_{AK} K,$$ (19)

where K – is the scale factor and equal to

$$K = \varphi R_0 \Delta R K_P K_i^2 \overline{K}_l \text{mm}^3/\text{V};$$ (20)

here φ – correction coefficient representing the inaccuracies of the designed analogue determined experimentally. The currents I_A, and I_B, determine the hypothetical reactions at the beam supports. For their determination it is only necessary to measure the potential difference between points A_{1-1}, and B_{1-n} (Fig. 3), and then the reactions $\overline{A}$ and $\overline{B}$ will be determined according to the formulae:

$$\overline{A} = \frac{U_{A_1-1}}{\Delta l} K;$$ (21)

$$\overline{B} = \frac{U_{B_1-n}}{\Delta l} K.$$ (22)

Determination of the Inaccuracy of the Analogue

We shall analyse the accuracy of the results obtained on this analogue.

Let us say that the beam is loaded with one concentrated force applied at the centre of the span. We shall analyse the simplified scheme of the analogue (Fig. 4). We shall introduce the following symbols:

δ — inaccuracy of the analogue in per cent during determination of deformations;

n — number of the sections of the beam;

λ — inaccuracy in the magnitude of the current in the analogue of the given beam in per cent;

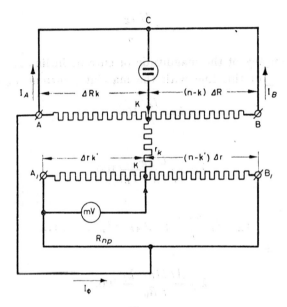

F<small>IG</small>. 4

η — inaccuracy in the magnitude of current of the hypothetical beam in per cent;

R_l — the internal resistance of the computing instrument in ohms;

I_{CK} — current of the line CK in amps;

I_l — current required by the computing instrument in amps;

U_{AK} — the voltage drop on line AK in volts;

I_A, I_B — currents modelling the reactions of the beam in amps;

31

k — the number of the section of the beam.

Using Kirchhoff's laws we have the following equations:

$$\left.\begin{aligned} I_{CK} &= I_A + I_B; \\ \frac{I_A}{I_B} &= \frac{n-k}{k}; \\ I_{AK} &= \frac{U_{AK}}{k \Delta R}; \end{aligned}\right\} \tag{23}$$

$$I_\Phi = \frac{U_{AK}}{R_0}. \tag{24}$$

The inaccuracy of the magnitude of current in line AB due to the loading of this line with the matching current I_Φ equals:

$$\lambda = \frac{I_\Phi}{I} 100$$

or

$$\lambda = \frac{U_{AK}}{R_0(I_A + I_B)} 100.$$

But as

$$I_A = I_B \frac{n-k}{k}; \quad U_{AK} = I_B(n-k)\Delta R,$$

then

$$\lambda = \frac{\Delta R k(n-k)}{n R_0} 100. \tag{25}$$

The inaccuracy of the current in line A_1 of resistance R_1 in consequence of the loading by the internal resistance R_r of the instrument is (in per cent)

$$\eta = \frac{I'_\Phi - I_\Phi}{I'_\Phi} 100, \tag{26}$$

where I'_Φ — supplied current of the line $A_1 B_1$ after reading the instrument

$$I'_\Phi = \frac{U_{AK}}{R'_0}; \tag{27}$$

32

here R_0' — resistance of the whole chain A_1K (Fig. 4) measured by the computing instrument.

Substituting (24) and (27) into (26), we obtain:

$$\eta = \frac{R_0 - R_0'}{R_0} \, 100. \tag{28}$$

The resistance of the whole chain A_1K (Fig. 4) comprises:

$$R_0' = r_k + \frac{\Delta r k' (n - k')}{k' + (n - k')\left(1 + \dfrac{\Delta r k'}{R_r}\right)}. \tag{29}$$

Bearing in mind (13), we obtain

$$R_0' = R_0 - \frac{\Delta r k (n - k)}{n} + \frac{\Delta r k' (n - k')}{k' + (n - k')\left(1 + \dfrac{\Delta r k'}{R_r}\right)}. \tag{30}$$

Substituting (30) into (28) we find:

$$\eta = \frac{\Delta r}{n R_0}\left[k(n - k) - \frac{k'(n - k)}{1 + \dfrac{(n - k')k'}{n} \times \dfrac{\Delta r}{R_r}} \right] 100. \tag{31}$$

The general inaccuracy of the analogue

$$\delta = \lambda + \eta = \frac{1}{n R_0}\left[k(n - k)(\Delta R + \Delta r) - \right.$$

$$\left. - \frac{\Delta r k' (n - k')}{1 + \dfrac{(n - k')k'\Delta r}{n R_r}} \right] 100. \tag{32}$$

We can easily see that the maximum inaccuracy will be, when $k = k^1 = n/2$ giving

$$\delta_{\max} = \frac{n}{4 R_0}\left[\Delta R + \frac{r \Delta r}{4 R_r\left(1 + \dfrac{r}{4 R_r}\right)} \right] 100. \tag{33}$$

Analogue of a Plain Beam

(a) *Beam of a variable profile*

Beams of variable profiles may also be calculated by means of the analysed analogue. In Fig. 5. we have a beam of variable profile and its electrical analogue. From the theory of grapho-analytic method of determining deformations it is known that

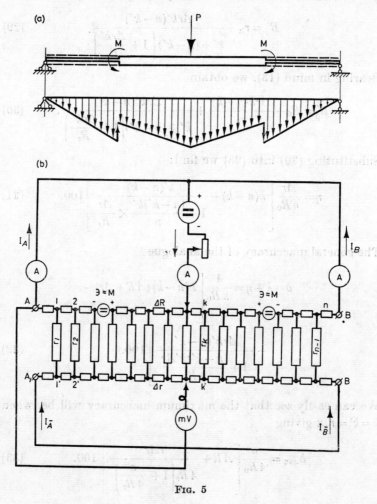

FIG. 5

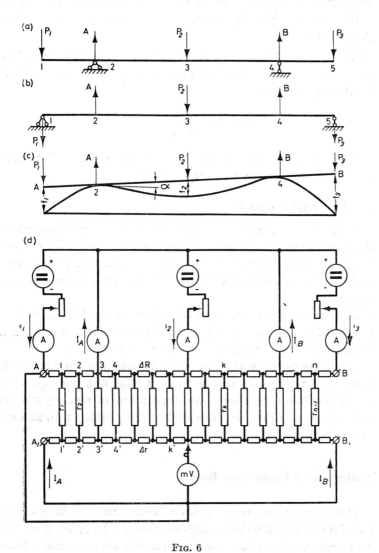

Fig. 6

the change of rigidity of the beam corresponds with the change of the curve of bending moments if we increase its ordinates $FI_0/EI(x)$ times.

From Fig. 5 it follows that this is equivalent to the application of two equal concentrated moments at the sections where the rigidity changes.

$$M = M_x\left(\frac{EI_0}{EI(x)} - 1\right).$$

These moments are analogous to the sources of voltage connected opposite each other (Fig. 5b).

(b) *Beam with a console*

An analogue of a plain beam with intermediary supports is also very simple to design as such a beam can be easily reduced to a beam without intermediary supports. In Fig. 6 we show a beam with two intermediary supports and its electrical analogue equivalent.

Here we must take into consideration that certain deflections are calculated from line AB (Fig. 6b) assuming the angle α is sufficiently small. In practice we proceed as follows.

The voltages measured on the analogue are transferred to graph paper. Through points 2 and 4 (Fig. 6b), corresponding to the position of supports, we draw a line of reading for AB, and normal to which we draw deflections f taking into account the scale (Fig. 6b).

Analogues of Continuous Beams

The above analogue of a plain beam can also be used for calculations of multispan continuous beams. In order to do this it is necessary to reduce the continuous beam to a basic, statically determinate beam on two supports, changing the intermediary supports into concentrated forces. In Fig. 7 we can see an example of a triple span beam and its analogue.

The additional unknown items (reactions B and C) are modelled by currents I_B and I_C.

The problem is solved as follows. To begin with we determine the currents i_1, i_2 and i_3 with the help of instruments. These currents are analogous to loads P_1, P_2 and P_3. Then we connect the required currents I_B and I_C their magnitude being regulated so that the hand of the galvanometer G (Fig. 7b) takes up zero position. This corresponds to the absence of the assumed moments at points B and C (that is deflections) and currents I_B and I_C determine the magnitude of reactions in B and C.

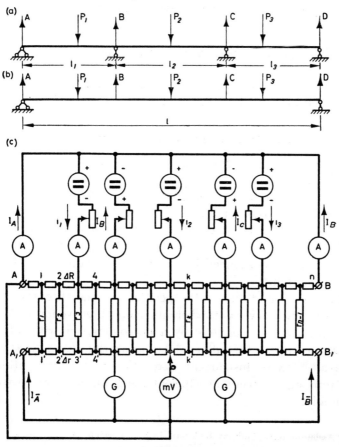

Fɪɢ. 7

This method is an analogue of the well known method of levelling deformations. It can be easily shown that continuous beams, having intermediate supports on different levels, may also be solved on this analogue. As in this case the vertical deformations of intermediate supports are given, so similarly voltages in points B and C are taken as known quantities. Then the selection of currents I_B and I_C is done in such a way that the given voltages are created at points B and C.

We conclude by saying that if the beam has an evenly distributed load, this load can be divided into numbers of equal concentrated forces, distributed along the section at equal distances.

Results of Experiments Made on the Analogue*

In order to prove the validity of the above theory an electrical analogue was constructed, the photograph of which can be seen in Fig. 8.

The data of this analogue are as follows:

$R_0 = 100\Omega$; $R = 0.087\Omega$; $r = 200\Omega$; $n = 20$;

$\Delta R = 0.00435\Omega$; $\Delta r = 10\Omega$. Resistances r_k were determined according to formula (13).

In order to verify the theory so far based on the usual methods of building mechanics, ordinates of elastic lines of a simple and continuous beam, loaded by one and two concentrated forces, were analysed.

In Figs. 9 and 10 are the positions of the theoretical and experimental curves of the bending moment curve for the beam. The voltage was measured by a micro-ammeter with internal resistance $R_x = 230\Omega$ adjusted for measuring e.m.f. Inaccuracies caused by the instrument were taken into consideration in the form of a correction coefficient which was calculated experimentally.

* Assistant K.D. Selikhov took part in the experiments.

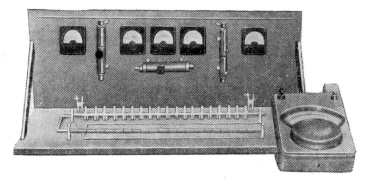

FIG. 8

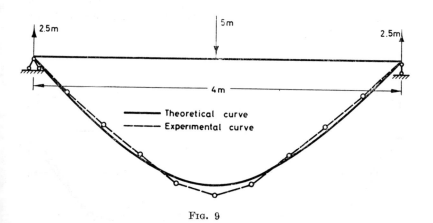

FIG. 9

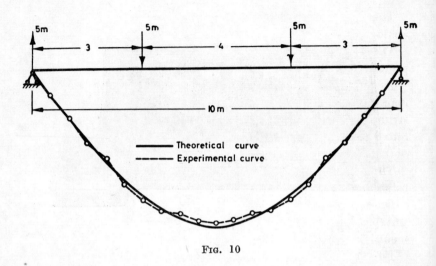

FIG. 10

In Fig. 11 the results of theoretical and experimental studies of a two-span continuous beam loaded with two concentrated forces are given.

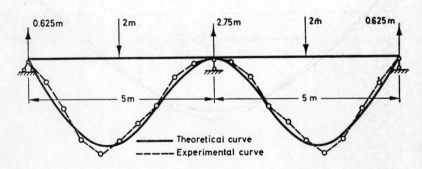

FIG. 11

Conclusions

The results of the experiment on the model verified the above analogy. The character of the curves of the bending beams is shown prominently on the analogue.

As far as the quantitative part of the problem is concerned, inaccurate choice of resistances r_k, and inaccuracy of the instrument itself, in some cases caused inaccuracies ranging from 5 to 8 per cent. But at this stage the problem was not posed to obtain accurate results.

The author's intention was to solve a basic problem and to establish whether the above theory would be feasible.

On the basis of this instrument it is possible to construct suitable computing instruments that would solve the above mentioned problems of building mechanics.

Finally the author would like to express his appreciation and thanks to the assistant of the Institute of Resistances of Materials K.D. Selikhova, who contributed greatly to the construction of the experimental instrument.

References

1. G.YE. PUKHOV, Application of electrical circuits to the problems of bending plane rod systems. *Electricity* No. 9. 1953.
2. P.M. CHEGOLIN, Application of methods of electro-mechanic similarities to the problem of calculating complex bending. Collection of articles *Analogues of beams and frameworks*. Taganrog. 1956.
3. O.V. IL'ENKO, Calculation and analogues of some spacial frameworks with the help of electrical circuits. Collection of articles *Analogues of beams and frameworks*. Taganrog. 1956.
4. V.N. STEPANOV, *Calculation of electrical circuits ONTI*. M.—L. 1933.
5. I.M. RABINOVICH, *Constructional mechanics of rod systems*. Stroiizdat. 1946.
6. R.H. RUSSEL, MacNeal unimproved electrical analogy for the analysis of beams in bending. *J. Appl. Mech.* **20**. No. 3. 1953.
7. C.W. RIESZ and B.I. SWAIN, *Structural analysis by electrical analogy. Proceedings of the Society for experimental stress analysis.* Vol. XII. No. 01. 1956.

4

ELECTRICAL ANALOGUE EMSS-1 FOR THE DESIGN OF BEAMS AND FRAMEWORKS

O.V. Il'enko and V.I. Usynin

WE KNOW [1, 2] that an active three terminal electrical 'T' network (Fig. 2) can serve as an analogy of a bending rod $1-2$ (Fig. 1). This analogue will be used in solving further problems. An electrical circuit, without negative resistances, proved to be more suitable to be used as an electrical analogue. The electrical circuit, shown in Fig. 4 [3] where T is the torque, can be used as the analogue of a twisted rod.

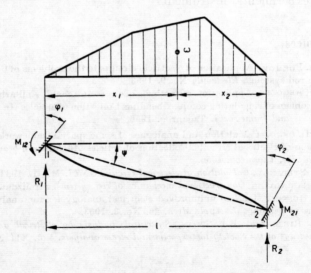

FIG. 1

42

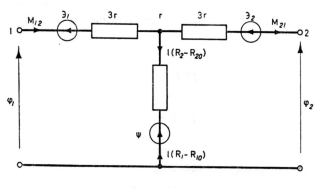

Fig. 2

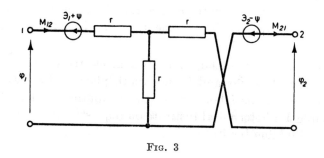

Fig. 3

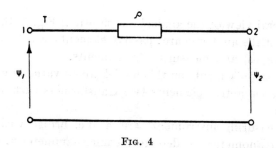

Fig. 4

The required parameters of the electrical circuit-analogue depend on the material, the size of the rod and the weight of the analysed system. These values can be obtained from the following equations:

$$\ni_1 = \frac{\omega x_1}{lEJ}\,; \quad \ni_2 = \frac{\omega x_2}{lEJ}\,; \tag{1}$$

$$r = \frac{l}{6EJ}\,; \quad \varrho = \frac{l}{GJ_k}\,. \tag{2}$$

Here EJ — rigidity in bending;
  G — modulus of elasticity for bar in torsion;
  J_k — inertia during torsion;
  l — length of the rod;
  x_1 and x_2 — distances from the left and right ends of the rod to the centre of gravity of the curve describing the bending moment, when the ends are freely pin-jointed.

Based on the described similarities, an electrical analogue for the design of beams and frames (both plane and special was constructed in the laboratory of the computing section of the Taganrog Radiotechnical Institute on request from the Rostov-on-Don Building Institute.

Short Description of Analogue EMSS-1

A general view of the analogue is shown in Fig. 5. Basic components of the analogue are: passive elements (rods), active elements (forces) and measuring instruments.

The passive elements on this model are 40 variable wire resistors, and the active elements two transformers each with nine windings.

The measuring instruments are a d.c. bridge with a type GMP galvanometer as detector, a micro-ammeter and a voltmeter.

The bridge is used to measure the magnitude of resistances which model parameters of the rod r [1]. The voltmeter together with the micro-ammeter type LM measure the magnitude and direction of e.m.f. (forces) and voltages (moments and angles of turn).

On the front vertical panel of the instrument is the dislocation circuit of the separate rods drawn on graph paper and placed under a sheet of glass, axes of the potentiometers and sockets for connecting.

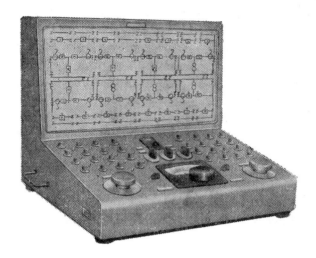

Fig. 5

On the front horizontal panel of the analogue are the switches for regulating the e.m.f.'s, selector switches, flip-flops, galvanometer, three decimal calibration resistances (hundred, ten and single units of ohms), micro-ammeter and gauging grooves.

The back and bottom cover of the instrument are detachable. The analogue is supplied from the 220 V a.c. mains. The maximum e.m.f. (parameters ∋) is 40 V, and the maximum resistance of the potentiometers is 1000 Ω. The inaccuracy of the analogue in relation to the results of calculations is ± (1–5 per cent). The inaccuracy is due to inaccuracy in the instruments when setting resistances and voltages.*

Operation of the Analogue

The work on the analogue consists of setting up the problem and the actual computing.

The setting up of the problem consists of:
(1) setting the resistances which model the magnitudes r of separate rods; (2) setting of the e.m.f.'s which model stresses; (3) design of the analogue-circuit.

The setting of the resistances and e.m.f. is done by comparitor circuits. The resistances are set using the standard of decimal resistances with the help of an indicator which changes when the resistance of the required potentiometer balances the bridge.

The required e.m.f. is set in the following manner: first the voltmeter is connected to the standard e.m.f. set equal to the required value, then using two switches, the e.m.f. to be used is increased to the required magnitude, a flip-flop indicating when they are equal. The circuit is connected up on the vertical panel using flexible leads. After connecting the analogue circuit the voltage is increased and electrical measurements taken.

Conclusions

The described analogue is very simple and sufficiently effective.

The operation of the instrument is simple and does not require special qualifications from the operator.

Study of rod systems using analogues is much quicker than analytic methods and the time saved increases with the complexity of problem.

---

* In the second alternative of the direct current analogue with a discrete selection of resistances and continuous setting for e.m.f., the fault does not exceed ± (0.5–2 per cent).

If necessary the number of modelling rods available can be increased by grouping several of the analogue machines described or by constructing a new machine for the given problem.

The analogue can be used in design for determination of the following factors (stress, dislocation of joints and supports, temperature, deformation of the foundation): (1) multi-span flitch and solid beams; (2) plane and spacial frames with dislocated and fixed joints; (3) beams crossed or broken in the plane.

References

1. G.Ye. Pukhov, *On the question of applying methods of electrical analogues to problems of bending plane beam systems.* Publishing House of the Tomsk Polytechnical Institute. **72**. Tomsk. 1952.
2. G.Ye. Pukhov, O.V. Il'enko and P.M. Chegolin, Electrical analogues of a bending rod. Collection of articles *Electrical analogues of beams and frameworks.* Taganrog. 1956.
3. O.V. Il'enko, Calculation and analogues of some three-dimensional frameworks with the help of electrical circuits with dislocation. Collection of articles *Electrical analogues of beams and frameworks.* Taganrog. 1956.

5

THE USE OF ITERATION IN ANALOGUES OF FRAMEWORKS USING A FOUR TERMINAL ACTIVE NETWORK*

V.I. Usynin

THE MODELLING of frames where angles of bending ψ are known does not cause any difficulties. [1, 2]. In cases where the angles of bending of the rods are not known and cannot be used as a basis for calculations we meet some difficulties if we want to use an analogue. For these cases we shall show below how iteration can help in introducing angles into the analogue.

This method is based on the principle of the three known equations of deformations. We introduce several approximate magnitudes of angles into the analogue until they practically converge and thus reach the solution of the problem.

The equations of the methods of deformations (equations of the reacting moments and transverse forces), having the following form (see e.g. [3] pp. 330 and 333).

$$\left[\sum_{ks}(2\,i_{mk}+1.5\,i_{ms})\right]\varphi_m + \sum_{k} i_{mk}\varphi_k - 3\sum_{k} i_{mk}\frac{\delta_{mk}}{l_{mk}} - $$
$$-1.5\sum_{s} i_{ms}\frac{\delta_{ms}}{l_{ms}} + \frac{1}{2}\sum M_m^P = 0. \qquad (1)$$

$$\sum \frac{i}{l}(\varphi_B + \varphi_H) - 2\sum \frac{i}{l^2}\delta + \sum \frac{(S+sl)}{6} + \frac{s'l}{12} + $$
$$+\sum \frac{S'v^2(3-2v)}{6} + \frac{Pcu'v'}{l} = 0, \qquad (2)$$

* Given at the 3rd scientific-technical conference of RTT 15th March 1957.

are used for our purpose in the following form:

$$3\sum_k i_{mk}\psi_{mk} + 1.5\sum_s i_{ms}\psi_{ms} = \frac{1}{2}\sum M^P\frac{1}{m_u} +$$

$$+ \left[\sum_{ks}(2i_{mk} + 1.5i_{ms})\right]\varphi_m \sum_k i_{mk}\varphi_k; \qquad (3)$$

$$\sum\frac{i}{l}\psi = \frac{1}{2}\sum\frac{i}{l}(\varphi_v + \varphi_1) + \frac{1}{2}\sum\frac{(S+sl)}{6m_u} +$$

$$+ \frac{s'l}{24m_u} + \frac{1}{2}\sum\frac{S'v^2(3-2v)}{6m_u} + \frac{Pcu'v'}{2lm_u} = 0. \qquad (4)$$

Here

m_u — scale of stress (voltage);

$$\psi_{mk} = \frac{\delta_{mk}}{l_{mk}}; \quad \psi_{ms} = \frac{\delta_{ms}}{l_{ms}}; \quad \psi = \frac{\delta}{l};$$

i_{mk} — coefficient of rigidity;

φ_m — the angle of deflection of the joint;

δ_{mk} — displacement of the ends of the bar butting against the joint;

M_m^P — reacting moment caused by the external stress;

Equations (3) and (4) are used for the introduction of iteration into the analogue as the unknown magnitudes of angles ψ.

This way, when modelling frames with unknown angles ψ, it is necessary, apart from the usual preparation of the problem, to rewrite equations (3) or (4); the stresses should be reduced to one term and substituted into the expression of e.m.f. ($\ni_i$ and $\ni_2$) for every bar which has ψ. Then we take the problem into the analogue and take $\psi = 0$. Then we measure the required φ (angles of deflection of the profiles) and substitute their magnitudes in (3) or (4). The obtained magnitudes ψ are introduced into the analogue angles again measured and so on and so forth until we obtain a practical convergence of the results. Finally we measure the required moments and angles of deflection.*

---

* Here, as well as in the preceding articles, when we speak of angles of deflection and moments we mean their analogies in the electrical circuits (i.e. currents and resistances).

According to the rules of constructional mechanics, it is recommended to use equation (3) in cases where the cross bars have hooks. In the remaining cases equation (4) should be used.

If the bars of the frames are pin jointed we must introduce a correction into equation (4) as it is written for cases with rods without pin-joints. For one support with one pin-joint on the upper end

$$\frac{1}{2}\sum \frac{i}{l}\,\psi = \frac{1}{2}\sum \frac{i}{l}\,\varphi^1 + \sum \frac{(S+sl)}{6m_u} + \frac{s'l}{16m_u} +$$

$$+ \sum S'\frac{v^2(3-v)}{12m_u} + \frac{Pc}{4lm_u}(1-u'^2);$$ (5)

TABLE 1

Sequence number of Iteration	φ_1	φ_2	φ_3	φ_2	φ_3	φ_4
1	23	14	5	24	7.5	3
2	35	30	10	43	18	6
3	45	44	17	56	27	12
4	51	56	24	66	37	16
5	56	65	31	74	46	21
6	60	74	38	82	54	26
7	64	82	45	89	61	34
8	68	89	51	96	67	40
9	71	96	56	97	71	46
10	72	98	61	100	72	49
11	73	100	63	101	78	51
12	75	105	65	102	83	52

TABLE 2

Moments in Fig. 1	Moments in mm		Relative error
	experimental	theoretical	
M_{12}	26	25.62	−1.48
M_{21}	4.36	4.38	+0.457
M_{23}	7.36	7.5	+1.87
M_{32}	10.75	10.5	−2.38
M_{34}	0.38	0.35	−9.4
M_{45}	6.24	6.32	+1.27
M_{27}	12.1	11.88	−1.85
M_{36}	10.4	10.18	−2.16

for a support with a pin-joint on the lower end

$$\frac{1}{2} \sum \frac{i}{l} \psi = \frac{1}{2} \sum \frac{i}{l} \varphi_\mathrm{B} + \sum \frac{(S+sl)}{6m_u} + \frac{5}{48m_u} s'l +$$

$$+ \sum S' \frac{v(3-v^2)}{12m_u} + \frac{Pc}{4lm_u}(1-v'^2). \tag{6}$$

The experiments of modelling frames, which had only wind load, have shown that it was necessary to perform approximately ten iterations. When modelling frames with vertical asymmetric loads the number of iterations was 2–3. It is necessary to mention that the number of iterations may be reduced if the process of iterations is not started with zero magnitudes of ψ but in some arbitrary magnitudes. On page 52 we show an example of modelling a frame.

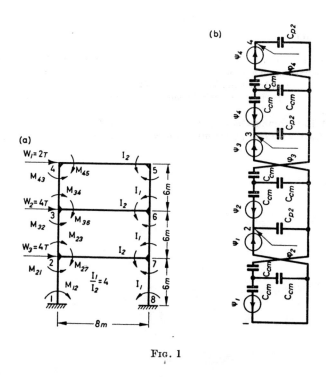

Fig. 1

EXAMPLE. To determine bending moments in joints and fastenings of a frame Fig. 1a.

Solution. In Fig. 1b is an analogue circuit of a frame (half only). On the basis of (4) we have the following equations for angles ψ:

$$\psi_1 = \frac{\varphi_2}{2} + 1.87 \ni \; ;$$

$$\psi_2 = \frac{\varphi_3 + \varphi_2}{2} + 1.12 \ni \; ;$$

$$\psi_3 = \frac{\varphi_4 + \varphi_3}{2} + 0.375 \ni .$$

Here $\ni = \dfrac{Pl_2^2}{16FJ} = 25$ V — voltage scale.

We shall introduce ψ_1, ψ_2, ψ_3 into the analogue by way of iteration. In Table 1 are shown magnitudes of iterations in volts and in Table 2 — comparison of magnitudes obtained by calculation and experiment

References

1. G.Ye. PUKHOV, *On the questions of applying methods of electrical analogues to the problems of bending plane beam systems.* Publishing House of the Tomsk Polytechnical Institute. **72.** Tomsk. 1952.
2. Collection of articles *Electrical analogues of beams and frameworks.* Taganrog. 1956.
3. I.M. RABINOVICH, *Course of structural mechanics.* Part 2. Gosstroiizdat. 1954.
4. G.V. UL'YANINSKII, *Calculation of frameworks in constructions.* Tomsk. 1931.

6

ELECTRICAL ANALOGUE OF
PLANE, STATICALLY
DETERMINED FRAMEWORK*

K.K. KEROPYAN

IN THE following article the methods given in the preceding chapter, will be further developed. We shall describe an experiment which constructs an analogue of a plane, statically determined girder and show how measurement of the currents flowing in the circuits of the analogue allow determination of the stresses in the bars of the given girder. Such a solution of this question in all its aspects shows the comparison between the construction of an electrical analogue and the Cremona diagram of stresses; which we shall do in our work [4].

Basic Description

In order to solve the given problem we shall utilize the analogy which can be made between the distribution of stresses in the parts of a girder and the distribution of currents in electrical circuits containing both resistive and reactive elements.

It is known that the geometrical sum of all stresses, applied to a joint of a balanced girder is always equal to zero. On the basis of this analogy it is possible to exchange the given statically determined girder comprised of n bars for an electrical analogue comprised of n circuits, in which the circuit admittances will model the length of a bar, and the phase angle of the

---

* Given at the joint session of the resistance of materials section and the constructional mechanics section of RISI 1st November 1956.

admittance the inclination of the bar to the vertical axis. The distribution of currents in elements of such an analogue will then correspond to the distribution of stresses in parts of the given girder.

We shall explain this using some simple examples.

In Fig. 1a we have inclined bars out of which a girder is usually composed and in Fig. 1b their analogues. The admittances of the circuits AB and BC Fig. 1b are:

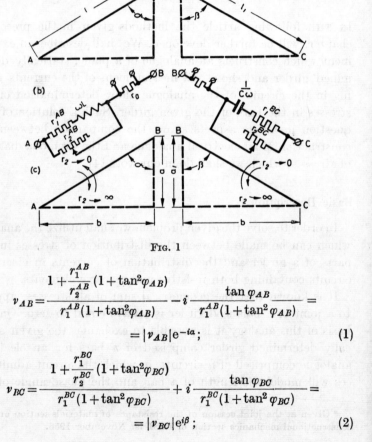

Fig. 1

$$v_{AB} = \frac{1 + \dfrac{r_1^{AB}}{r_2^{AB}}(1 + \tan^2\varphi_{AB})}{r_1^{AB}(1 + \tan^2\varphi_{AB})} - i\frac{\tan\varphi_{AB}}{r_1^{AB}(1 + \tan^2\varphi_{AB})} =$$

$$= |v_{AB}|e^{-ia}; \tag{1}$$

$$v_{BC} = \frac{1 + \dfrac{r_1^{BC}}{r_2^{BC}}(1 + \tan^2\varphi_{BC})}{r_1^{BC}(1 + \tan^2\varphi_{BC})} + i\frac{\tan\varphi_{BC}}{r_1^{BC}(1 + \tan^2\varphi_{BC})} =$$

$$= |v_{BC}|e^{i\beta}; \tag{2}$$

$$\left. \begin{aligned} \tan \varphi_{AB} &= \frac{\omega L}{r_1^{AB}}; \\[2mm] \tan \varphi_{BC} &= \frac{1}{r_1^{BC}\omega C}. \end{aligned} \right\} \qquad (3)$$

This is illustrated in Fig. 1b, where the length b is the imaginary part of ν_{AB} and the length a the real part of ν_{AB}.

If the two bars are of equal length then $b_1 = b$ i.e.

$$r_1^{BC}\tan \varphi_{AB}(1 + \tan^2 \varphi_{BC}) = r_1^{AB}\tan \varphi_{BC}(1 + \tan^2 \varphi_{AB}). \qquad (4)$$

Then using (3), we can find the required frequency of the current:

$$\omega = \sqrt{\left(\frac{L - C(r_1^{AB})^2}{LC[L - C(r_1^{BC})^2]} \right)}. \qquad (5)$$

Further, if $r_1^{AB} = r_1^{BC}$, then (5) becomes

$$\omega = \frac{1}{\sqrt{(LC)}} \qquad (6)$$

and the phase angles

$$\varphi_{AB} = \varphi_{BC} = \varphi. \qquad (6a)$$

Later when calculating equal-panelled girders, we shall assume that condition (6) is fulfilled.

Phase angle of the circuit AC

$$\tan \alpha = \frac{\tan \varphi_{AB}}{1 + \dfrac{r_1^{BC}}{r_2^{AB}}(1 + \tan^2 \varphi_{AB})}. \qquad (7)$$

Phase angle of circuit BC

$$\tan \beta = \frac{\tan \varphi_{BC}}{1 + \dfrac{r_1^{BC}}{r_2^{BC}}(1 + \tan^2 \varphi_{BC})}. \qquad (8)$$

Resistance r_0 serves for measuring the energy of the current feeding the circuit and should be very small in comparison with r_1 in order not to cause inaccuracies.

It follows from formulae (1) and (2) that by changing the magnitude of the variable resistance r_2, it is possible to change the angles α and β. We must mention that in the course of this, only the conductance (real part of the admittance) of the circuit changes whereas the susceptance (imaginary part of the admittance) remains constant.

If $r_1 \neq 0$, then changing r_2 in the range 0 to ∞, changes the admittances in the range:

$$v_{AB} = \left[\infty \div \frac{1}{r_1^{AB}(1 + \tan^2 \varphi_{AB})} - j \frac{\tan \varphi_{AB}}{r_1^{AB}(1 + \tan^2 \varphi_{AB})} \right]; \qquad (9)$$

$$v_{BC} = \left[\infty \div \frac{1}{r_1^{BC}(1 + \tan^2 \varphi_{BC})} + j \frac{\tan \varphi_{BC}}{r_1^{BC}(1 + \tan^2 \varphi_{BC})} \right] \qquad (10)$$

and phase angles

$$0 < \alpha < \varphi_{AB}, \quad 0 < \beta < \varphi_{BC}. \qquad (10a)$$

We shall analyse the elastic system comprised of two bars (Fig 2a) and its electrical analogue (Fig. 2b).

The stresses in the bars will be found by taking the sum of projections of all forces on the axes X and Y:

$$\left. \begin{array}{l} N_1 \sin \alpha - N_2 \sin \alpha = 0; \\ N_1 \cos \alpha + N_2 \cos \alpha = P. \end{array} \right\} \qquad (11)$$

From which

$$N_1 = N_2 = \frac{P}{2 \cos \alpha}. \qquad (12)$$

Now consider the analogue. We control the magnitude of the resistance r_2 in such a way that the phase angles equal the given magnitudes. From formulae (7) and (8), and knowing angles α and β, we can easily find the magnitude of r_2.

From Kirchhoff's law we have the following vector equation:

$$I = I_1 e^{ia} + I_2 e^{-ia} \qquad (13)$$

or

$$I = I_1(\cos \alpha + i \sin \alpha) + I_2(\cos \alpha - i \sin \alpha). \qquad (14)$$

Dividing (14) into real and imaginary parts we obtain the following equations:

$$I_1 \sin \alpha - I_2 \sin \alpha = 0;$$
$$I_1 \cos \alpha + I_2 \cos \alpha = I, \qquad (15)$$

solving we find:

$$I_1 = I_2 = \frac{I}{2 \cos \alpha}. \qquad (16)$$

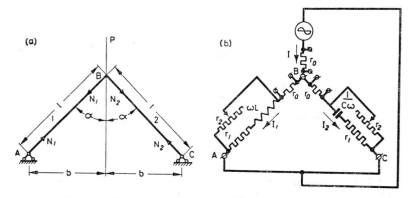

FIG. 2

The last result equals (12).

Let the elastic system be asymmetric (Fig. 3).

The circuit of the electrical analogue will remain the same as in the previous case. However, the parameters of the circuits will change. We shall analyse the system of Fig. 3a. Here the distances b and c are different. Consequently, the susceptances of both branches will differ and can be determined from a geometrical similarity. After simple transformations we have:

$$k = \frac{b}{c} = \frac{L[(r_1^{BC} \omega C)^2 + 1]}{C[(r_1^{AB})^2 + (\omega L)^2]}, \qquad (17)$$

from which the required frequency of the current will be:

$$\omega = \sqrt{\left(\frac{L - kC(r_1^{AB})^2}{LC[kL - C(r_1^{BC})^2]} \right)}. \qquad (18)$$

The resistances r_2 are controlled in both branches so that the relation

$$\frac{l_1}{l_2} = \frac{|v_1|}{|v_2|} \tag{19}$$

is preserved.

The system of Fig. 3b is dealt with in a similar way.

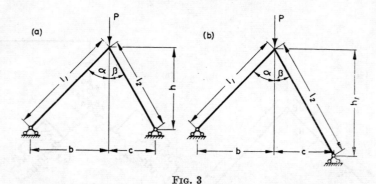

FIG. 3

We shall analyse as a further example the girder and its analogue depicted in Fig. 4. Correct adjustment of the analogue is done by controlling the resistances r_2 of each circuit so that the phase angles will become equal to the given proportions.

We shall find the stresses in the elements of the girder. By summation of the forces at the joints. Writing the equations in the complex form:

$$\left.\begin{array}{l} X_1 e^{ia} + X_3 e^{-ia} + X_5 = P; \\ X_1 e^{ia} + X_2 e^{i\beta} = A; \\ X_3 e^{-ia} + X_4 e^{-i\beta} = C; \\ X_2 e^{i\beta} + X_4 e^{-i\beta} = X_5. \end{array}\right\} \tag{20}$$

Dividing (20) into real and imaginary parts we obtain a system of equations giving the stresses in the bars of the girder:

$$X_1 = X_3 = \frac{P}{2\left(\cos \alpha - \dfrac{\sin \alpha}{\tan \beta}\right)}; \tag{21}$$

$$X_2 = X_4 = -\frac{P\dfrac{\sin\alpha}{\sin\beta}}{2\left(\cos\alpha - \dfrac{\sin\alpha}{\tan\beta}\right)} \; ; \qquad (22)$$

$$X_5 = -\frac{P\dfrac{\sin\alpha}{\tan\beta}}{\cos\alpha - \dfrac{\sin\alpha}{\tan\beta}} . \qquad (23)$$

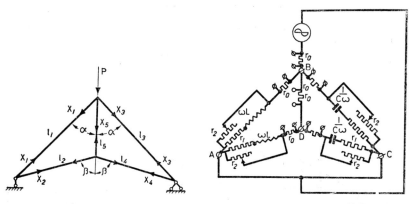

Fig. 4

From the first law of Kirchhoff for nodes A, B, C, D of the analogue, it is possible to write in complex form the following equations:

$$\left.\begin{aligned}
&I_1 e^{ia} + I_3 e^{-ia} + I_5 = I; \\
&I_1 e^{ia} + I_2 e^{i\beta} = I_A; \\
&I_3 e^{-ia} + I_4 e^{-i\beta} = I_C; \\
&I_2 e^{i\beta} + I_4 e^{-i\beta} = I_5.
\end{aligned}\right\} \qquad (24)$$

These equations are identical with equations (20).

Currents I_A and I_C in equations (24) are taken as active and acting in antiphase to the external load. The sources of these currents are not shown in Fig. 4 and 5. During operation of the analogue the relations between currents through the elements

59

of the analogue and the current I (force P) will not correspond
with the relations of stresses in the bars of the girder (Fig. 4)
to the load P. In order to obtain correct results it is necessary
to compute doubled current of the centre bar from the general
current I_S measured on the analogue, which follows from a
comparison of the vector diagram of currents for the whole analogue and the diagram of stresses (Cremona).

The study of this problem on an experimental analogue
proved the above-mentioned drawings.

Proceeding in a similar way we obtain the solutions:

$$I_1 = I_3 = \frac{I}{2\left(\cos\alpha - \dfrac{\sin\alpha}{\tan\beta}\right)};\qquad(25)$$

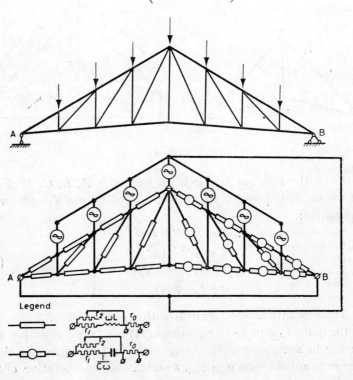

Legend

Fig. 5

60

$$I_2 = I_4 = -\frac{I\dfrac{\sin\alpha}{\sin\beta}}{2\left(\cos\alpha - \dfrac{\sin\alpha}{\tan\beta}\right)};\qquad(26)$$

$$I_5 = -\frac{I\dfrac{\sin\alpha}{\tan\beta}}{\cos\alpha - \dfrac{\sin\alpha}{\tan\beta}}.\qquad(27)$$

These expressions fully correspond with (21), (22) and (23). Using the method described for the analogues of bars (depicted in Fig. 1) it is possible to construct an analogue of any statically determined girder. In Fig. 5, a more complex girder and its analogue are shown.

It is believed that the above principles for constructing an analogue of a statically determined girder could serve as a basis for constructing a universal computing machine with the help of which it would be possible to design and calculate various girders and similar constructions.

References

1. L.I. GUTENMAKHER, *Electrical analogues.* Publishing House of the Academy of Sciences of the U.S.S.R. 1949.
2. N.M. TETEL'BAUM. *Study of torsional vibrations of piston engine rollers with the help of electrical analogues.* Publishing House BNT. 1948.
3. G.Ye. PUKHOV, Application of electrical circuits to the problem of bending plane rod systems. *Electricity.* No. 9. 1953.
4. K.K. KEROPYAN, On the design of statically determined frameworks calculated with the help of electrical analogues. Collection of articles *Electrical analogues of beams and frameworks.* Taganrog. 1956.

7

CALCULATION OF THE EFFECTS OF TEMPERATURE ON BEAMS AND PLANE FRAMEWORKS USING ELECTRICAL ANALOGUE CIRCUITS*

O.V. Il'enko

WHEN studying the effects of temperature on girders and plane frames with the help of electrical analogues, the same three terminal networks can be used as were used in the calculation of the effects of external forces.† The required resistances of the electrical circuits are determined from the usual formula

$$r = \frac{l}{6FJ}. \tag{1}$$

The effect of temperature on specific rod systems requires evaluation of the e.m.f.'s $\ni_1 \ni_2$ and ψ.

Regular rise in temperature causes either lengthening or shortening of the rod as all its threads heat or cool regularly. The change in length of only one rod of an entire construction generally leads to dislocation of the ends of one or m ny other rods of the construction, which eventually shows itself in the change of e.m.f. (ψ) on electrical analogues of these systems. The change in length is determined from the formula

$$\Delta = \alpha t l_1, \tag{2}$$

* Given on 26th February 1957 at the 13th scientific-technical conference of RISI.

† See (3) in the literature section of the preceding article.

where α — coefficient of linear expansion;
t — change in temperature of the rod;
l_1 — length of the heated rod.

The magnitude ψ, characterizing the displacement of the ends of one rod and causing proportional heating in the next rod, is determined from the following relation

$$\psi = \frac{\Delta}{l_2}, \tag{3}$$

where l_2 — length of the rod of which the ends are mutually dislodged.

In an irregular change of temperature the rods not only change in length but also get distorted as the threads of the one and the same profile heat or cool differently. Therefore an irregular heating on the electrical analogue will be expressed in general by connecting the e.m.f. corresponding to ψ, and $\ni_1, \ni_2$, $\ni_1$ and $\ni_2$ are connected into the network modelling the rod to analyse the irregular heating (over the height) as well as the e.m.f., corresponding to ψ, connected into the network due to the displacement at the ends produced by the other heated rod connected at this point.

The magnitudes $\ni_1$ and $\ni_2$ are determined from the formulae

$$\ni_1 = \ni_2 = \alpha \frac{\Delta t}{h} \times \frac{l}{2}, \tag{4}$$

where $\Delta t = t_1 - t_u$ — difference in temperature of the upper and lower thread of the rod;
h — the height of the rod;
l — the length of the rod.

The change in length of the irregularly heated rod can be found from the formula

$$\Delta = \alpha \frac{t_1 + t_u}{2} l. \tag{5}$$

When choosing electrical analogues of separate rods systems calculated on temperature analytically, or using electrical analogue, we must follow the same considerations as in calculating similar systems on external influences.

To verify the above we shall give as an example the calculating of the bending moments in a frame influenced by various temperatures.

EXAMPLE.* We calculate a frame (Fig. 1) with irregular heating of the cross bar: top $-10°$ low end $+30°$ and regular heating of supports on $+30°$. The frame is of reinforced concrete coefficient of linear temperature expansion $\alpha = 1.10^{-5}$. Temperature of the surrounding section $t_0 = 0°$.

Height of the cross bar section: in outer spans $h_m = 100$ cm, in the middle span $h_m = 110$. Rigidity taken in a unit $EJ = 2.10$ Ton. metres. Related rigidities

$$EJ_{1-4} = EJ_{2-5} = 1.5; \quad EJ_{3-4} = EJ_{5-6} = 3; \quad EJ_{4-5} = 4.$$

Lengths of the rods:

$$l_1 = 12 \text{ m}; \, l_2 = 16 \text{ m}; \, l_3 = 9 \text{ m}.$$

Solution. We shall design the electrical circuit of the frame. The regular rise in temperature causes lengthening of the supports by Δ_c. Joints 4 and 5 are lifted, that is a mutual dislocation of the cross bar's spans $3-4$ and $5-6$ will take place. Therefore the networks, modelling the spans $3-4$ and $5-6$ will have e.m.f. and the corresponding ψ.

Also joints 4 and 5 will lift by the same magnitude and spans $3-4$ and $5-6$ will be of equal length, and e.m.f., and corresponding ψ (we shall denote them as ψ_p) connected into the networks $3-4$ and $5-6$ must be equal in magnitude. Apart from that, e.m.f. $\ni(\ni_1)$ will enter the network as the cross bar is irregularly heated. For the same reason e.m.f. $\ni(\ni_2)$ will enter the network modelling span $4-5$.

The middle span of the cross bar $4-5$ will lengthen, thus the upper end of the support $1-4$ will be shifted to the left and supports $2-5$ to the right by an equal magnitude of half Δ_p.

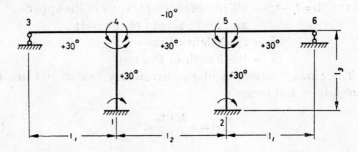

FIG. 1

* [4], P. 42.

Calculation of Effects of Temperature

Because of the symmetry of the construction and temperature influence, only one half of the whole electrical circuit of the frame is used for both analytical and electrical calculations. (Fig. 2) We shall find the parameters of the electrical circuit:

$$\vartheta_1 = \frac{\alpha(t_1 - t_u)}{h_k} \frac{l_{3-4}}{2} = \frac{1 \times 10^{-5}(30+10)}{100} \frac{1200}{2} = 240 \times 10^{-5} \text{ degrees;}$$

$$\vartheta_2 = \frac{\alpha(t_1 - t_u)}{h_m} \frac{l_{4-5}}{2} = \frac{1 \times 10^{-5}(30+10)}{110} \frac{1600}{2} = 291 \times 10^{-5} \text{ degrees.}$$

Lengthening of the supports

$$\Delta_c = \frac{\alpha(t_1 - t_u)}{2} l_{1-4} = \frac{1 \times 10^{-5}(30+30)}{2} 9 = 270 \times 10^{-5} \text{ degrees.}$$

Then

$$\varphi_p = \frac{\Delta_c}{l_{3-4}} = \frac{270 \times 10^{-5}}{12} = 22.5 \times 10^{-5} \text{ degrees.}$$

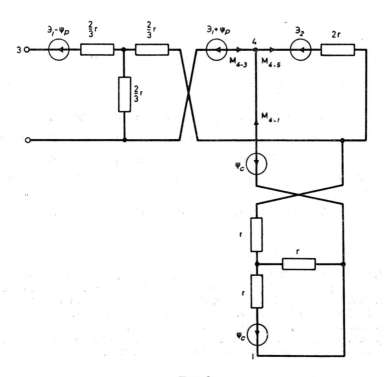

Fig. 2

Lengthening of the span of the cross bar

$$\Delta_p = \frac{\alpha(t_1 + t_u)}{2} l_{4-5} = \frac{1 \times 10^{-5}(30-10)}{2} 16 = 160 \times 10^{-5} \text{ degrees m.}$$

Therefore

$$\psi_c = \frac{\Delta_p}{2l_{1-4}} = \frac{160 \times 10^{-5}}{2 \times 9} = 8.9 \times 10^{-5} \text{ degrees.}$$

Resistances:

$$r_{1-4} = r_{2-4} = \frac{l_{1-4}}{6EJ \times 1.5} = \frac{1}{EJ} \text{ (kgcm)}^{-1};$$

$$r_{3-4} = l_{5-6} = \frac{l_{3-4}}{6EJ \times 3} = \frac{2}{3EJ} \text{ (kgcm)}^{-1};$$

$$r_{4-5} = \frac{l_{4-5}}{6EJ \times 4} = \frac{2}{3EJ} \text{ (kgcm)}^{-1}.$$

We shall denote

$$\frac{1}{EJ} = r.$$

Then

$$r_{1-4} = r_{2-4} = r; \quad r_{3-4} = r_{4-5} = r_{5-6} = \frac{2}{3} r.$$

Calculating the system by the conversion method (from the analogue we shall obtain the following magnitudes of moments:

$$M_{4-3} = -34.7 \text{ mm}; \quad M_{4-5} = -32.3 \text{ mm}; \quad M_{4-1} = 2.4 \text{ mm.}$$

If the method of forces, used in [4] is employed we get the following results:

$$M_{4-3} = -34.66 \text{ mm}; \quad M_{4-5} = 32.24 \text{ mm}; \quad M_{4-1} = 2.42 \text{ mm.}$$

When solving the problem on the analogue EMSS-1 the following results were obtained:

$$M_{4-3} = -34.55 \text{ mm}; \quad M_{4-5} = 31.8 \text{ mm}; \quad M_{4-1} = 2.45 \text{ mm.}$$

References

1. G.YE. PUKHOV, O.V. IL'ENKO and P.W. CHEGOLIN, Electrical analogues of bending rods. *Electrical analogues of beams and frameworks*. Taganrog. 1956.
2. O.V. I'LENKO and V.I. USYNIN, Electrical analogue EMSS-1 for calculating beams and frameworks. Article in the present collection.
3. S.A. ROGITSKII, *Design of frames*. Mashgiz. 1948.
4. B.N. ZHEMOCHKIN and D.P. PUSHCHEVSKII, *Statics of constructions*, Government Publishing House of Architecture. 1950.

8

AN ELECTRICAL CIRCUIT
FOR SIMULATING A COMPLICATEDLY
BENT CONICAL BEAM*

P.M. CHEGOLIN

THE METHOD of electrical analogues is often used in solving the problems of building mechanics. Further development of the experimental method requires study of simple electrical circuits replacing various deformed constructions. The three terminal circuit replacing a bent rod, worked out by Prof. Pukhov [1] in 1952 proved very simple and practical. Later, a similar circuit was designed by the author of this article for a complicated prismoidal camber bar statically loaded.

A number of constructions (e.g. pillars, radio masts) can be analysed as conic beams, bending under the influence of their own weight and external forces in a complicated way. Many conical parts of machines work under similar conditions. Electrical analogues of such construction enable us to replace calculations by an immediate determination (reading) of stresses and deformations on the instruments of the analogue.

Analogues of complicated camber beams have another interesting feature. Let us say that the bending bar is positioned in a continuous elastic medium with a coefficient of rigidity k, characterizing the resistance of the medium to the twisting of the bar; in this case the elastic line will be described by the following differential equation

$$\frac{d^4y}{dx^4} - \frac{k}{EJ}\frac{d^2y}{dx^2} = 0.$$

* Given at the 12th session of the scientific-technical conference of RISI on 7th March 1956.

This equation in its external form corresponds to the differential equation of a complicated bending:

$$\frac{d^4y}{dx^4} + \frac{N}{EJ}\frac{d^2y}{dx^2} = 0,$$

with the difference that $N = -k$. Consequently, it is possible to use an electrical analogue of a complicated camber bar without any changes in order to study the bending of the bar in a continuous elastic medium.

Finally, the study of an electrical circuit replacing a complicated camber bar provides the main basis for experimental research in complicated bending of bars with variable profile.

Let us suppose that bar 1-2 (Fig. 1a) is isolated from the system in such a way that it has no external load and the influence of the system is accounted for by bending moments at the ends $M1$ and $M2$ and the reactions Q. In this case [3] the dependence between the angles of turn of the end profiles and the bending moments $M1$ and $M2$ can be expressed in the following form:

$$\left.\begin{array}{l} \varphi_1 = M_1\dfrac{l}{3EJ_0}\times\dfrac{n}{n-1}\,\Psi(u) + M_2\dfrac{l}{6EJ_0}\left(\dfrac{n}{n-1}\right)^2\Phi(u) + \gamma; \\[2mm] -\varphi_2 = M_1\dfrac{l}{6EJ_0}\left(\dfrac{n}{n-1}\right)^2\Phi(u) + M_2\dfrac{l}{3FJ_0}\left(\dfrac{n}{n-1}\right)^3\Psi(u) - \gamma, \end{array}\right\} \quad (1)$$

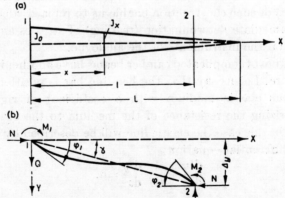

FIG. 1

where

$$\Phi(u) = \frac{3}{u}\left(\frac{1}{\sin\ 2u} - \frac{1}{2u}\right); \quad \Psi(u) = \frac{3}{2u}\left(\frac{1}{2u} - \frac{1}{\tan\ 2u}\right); \quad (2)$$

$$u = \frac{n}{n-1} \times \frac{l}{2}\sqrt{\left(\frac{N}{EJ_0}\right)}; \quad n = \frac{L}{l}; \quad (3)$$

here L — abscissa of the apex of the cone (Fig. 1a);

l — length of the bar;

N — horizontal end thrust;

J_0 — inertia of the profile at the beginning;

E — modulus elasticity of the material of the bar;

$\gamma = \frac{\Delta y}{l}$ — intersection angle, characterizing the relative displaced positions of the ends 1 and 2.

If expanding forces influence the bar then u is an imaginary number and the functions of influence $\Psi(u)$ and $\Phi(u)$ become:

$$\Psi_0(u) = \frac{3}{2u}\left(\frac{1}{\tanh\ 2u} - \frac{1}{2u}\right), \quad \Phi_0(u) = \frac{3}{u}\left(\frac{1}{2u} - \frac{1}{\sinh\ 2u}\right). \quad (4)$$

If the angles of turn in equations (1) are treated as voltage, and the bending moments as currents, then we can easily see that three terminal electrical network corresponds with these

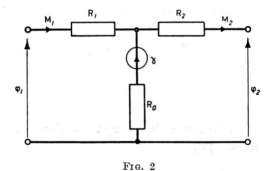

Fig. 2

69

equations (Fig. 2). This network is fully determined by the relationships.

$$R_0 = -\frac{l}{6EJ_0}\left(\frac{n}{n-1}\right)^2 \Phi(u);$$

$$R_1 = \frac{l}{6EJ_0}\frac{n}{n-1}\left[2\Psi(u)+\frac{n}{n-1}\,\Phi(u)\right];$$

$$R_2 = \frac{l}{6EJ_0}\left(\frac{n}{n-1}\right)^2\left[\frac{n}{n-1}\,2\Psi(u)+\Phi(u)\right],$$

(5)

these values being the parameters of the modelling circuit. As would be expected, the analogue is asymmetric unlike the analogue of a prismoidal bar. The functions $\Psi(u)$ and $\Phi(u)$ are tabulated therefore the parameters (5) can be easily determined, if the horizontal force, geometric and elastic characteristics of the conical bar are given.

We shall mention that in the case of a prismoidal bar $n = L/l = \infty$ and then equation (1) takes the form:

$$\varphi_1 = M_1\frac{l}{3EJ}\Psi(u)+M_2\frac{l}{6EJ}\,\Phi(u)+\gamma;$$

$$-\varphi_2 = M_1\frac{l}{6EJ}\Phi(u)+M_2\frac{l}{3EJ}\,\Psi(u)-\gamma.$$

(6)

The analogue is made symmetrical with parameters:

$$R_1 = R_2 = \frac{l}{2FJ}\times\frac{\tan u}{u};$$

(7)

$$R_0 = \frac{l}{6EJ}\,\Phi(u).$$

The equations (6) were obtained by the author on an analogue of prismoidal bars [2].

References

1. G.Ye. PUKHOV, *On the question of applying methods of electrical analogues into the problems of bending plane beam systems*. Publishing House of the Tomsk Polytechnical Institute. 72. Tomsk. 1952.
2. P.M. CHEGOLIN, The application of electromechanical similarities to the problem of complex bending. Collection of articles *Electrical analogues of beams and frameworks*. Taganrog. 1956.
3. B.F. NEUSTROYEV, On the question of testing the stability of plane rod systems with applied stress in joints. Collection of articles *Research in the theory of constructions*. Fasc. VI. Gosstroiizdat. 1954.

9

THE CALCULATION OF THE DEFLECTION OF PILLARS' FOUNDATIONS WITH THE HELP OF ELECTRICAL ANALOGUES OF FRAMEWORKS*

G.YE. PUKHOV and O.V. IL'ENKO

AN IMPORTANT problem of building mechanics is the calculation of the influence of deflection of the supports foundations on the distribution of stresses in frame constructions. Below we show how it is possible to solve this problem using an electrical analogue where the analogue of every bar is represented by a three terminal active electrical network or if the bar forms a closed system, as an electrical 'T' network [2, 3].

We shall assume that the ends of all the supports are fixed in separate foundations and the foundations themselves will be taken as rigid and built on an elastic soil.

Under the influence of the bending moment M transmitted from the support to the foundation, the latter will turn through an angle φ. Within the case of a linear dependence between deformation and tension we can write that

$$\varphi = \varrho M, \tag{1}$$

where the constant coefficient ϱ depends on the dimensions and shape of the foundation (right-angled, square, etc.), on the place where the support is fixed, and on the elastic properties of the soil.

* Given at the 12th scientific-technical conference of RISI 7th March 1956.

The angle of turn of the foundation can be treated as voltage and the moment M, twisting the foundation, as an electric current; the expression (1) is analogous to Ohm's Law in the case of a passive network ($u = Ri$, where u – voltage, i – current and R – resistance) and, consequently, the elastic properties of the soil, the dimensions and shape of the foundation can be represented on the electrical analogue by resistances ϱ calculation on a transitional scale connecting points, corresponding to the support's fixing points. The magnitude ϱ will be called a parameter of the fixing. It can be determined either on the basis of experimental data or by way of correlated calculations. We shall use some known formulae for determining the magnitude of the parameter of fixing.

According to the hypothesis of Winkler, the normal reaction of the soil at an arbitrary point underneath the foundation is proportional to the sinking at that point; therefore the dependence between φ and M takes the form:

$$\varphi = \frac{M}{c_\varphi J_\Phi}. \tag{2}$$

Comparing (2) and (1) we can see that in the given case

$$\varrho = \frac{1}{c_\varphi J_\Phi}, \tag{3}$$

where c_φ – a coefficient of the foundation, and J_Φ – the moment of inertia of the foundation about an axis perpendicular to the plane of turning of the foundation.

Using the theory of elasticity, V. V. Nikolayev [1] obtained the following formula for rectangular foundations with sides a and b

$$\varphi = \frac{kM}{b^3 E_d}. \tag{4}$$

Comparing (4) and (1), we see that

$$\varrho = \frac{k}{b^3 E_d}. \tag{5}$$

Here b — the width of the foundation;

E_d — given modulus of elasticity for the deformation of the soil;

k — non-dimensional coefficient, its magnitude depending on the value $\alpha = a/b$,

where a — length of the foundation.

Magnitudes k are given in [1].

K.Ye. Yegorov obtained the following formula for circular foundations

$$\varphi = \frac{3}{4} \frac{M}{R^3 E_d} \tag{6}$$

where R — radius of the circular foundation.

Consequently, for the circular foundations

$$\varrho = \frac{3}{4 R^3 E_d}. \tag{7}$$

To conclude we shall analyse as an example the calculation of the twist of the foundations of a Π-shaped frame (Fig. 1) with the help of an electrical analogue.

Given data*: $l = 18$ m; $h = 8$ m; $q = 2$ tons/m; $J_1 = 5.8 \times 10^4$ cm^4; J_2 61.2×10^4 cm^4; the foundation is square with sides $a = b = = 1.7$ m; $k = 4.4$ argillaceous soil; modulus of elasticity for the deformation of the soil $E_d = 455$ kg/cm^2; and for the material of the frame E $2.1 = 10^6$ kg/cm^2. The required parameters of the electrical analogue-circuit are determined from the following formulae:

$$r_1 = \frac{h}{6EJ_1}; \quad r_2 = \frac{l}{6EJ_2}; \quad \varrho = \frac{k}{b^3 E_d}; \quad \Im = \frac{ql^3}{24EJ_2}.$$

Substituting numerical quantities we obtain:

$$r_1 = 4.69 r_2; \quad \varrho = 8.44 r_2; \quad \Im = 162 r_2.$$

* The data are taken from the work by V.V. Nikolayev [1].

Bearing in mind the symmetry of the system it is easy to observe that the bending moments M_A and M_B are determined from formulae:

$$M_B = -\frac{\ni}{r_\Sigma}; \quad M_A = -M_B \frac{r_1}{2r_1 + \varrho},$$

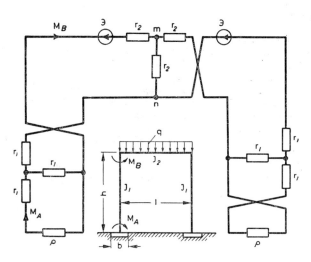

FIG. 1

where

$$r_\Sigma = 3r_2 + r_1 + \frac{r_1(r_1 + \varrho)}{2r_1 + \varrho}.$$

Substituting numerical quantities we obtain.

$$r_\Sigma = 11.1r_2; \quad M_A = 3.83 \text{ mm}; \quad M_B = 14.6 \text{ mm}.$$

The circuit was set up on the analogue described in [4]. The results of measuring were:

$$M_A = 3.84 \text{ mm}; \quad M_B = -14.5 \text{ mm}.$$

In [1] for the given example, the following results were obtained by calculation

$$M_A = -3.24 \text{ mm}; \quad M_B = 14.9 \text{ mm}.$$

The difference in sign is explained by different positive directions of the bending moments, and the difference in magnitudes of the moments by the fact that calculation using the formulae given in [1] are less accurate due to their complicated structure.

References

1. V.V. NIKOLAYEV, The influence of deformations in foundations on the stress of U-shaped frameworks. Collection of articles *Questions of constructional mechanics*. Government Publishing House of Literature on Civil Engineering and Architecture. Moscow 1953.
2. G.Ye. PUKHOV, *On the question of applying methods of electrical analogues to the problems of bending plane beam systems*. Publishing House of the Tomsk Polytechnical Institute **72**. Tomsk. 1952.
3. G.Ye. PUKHOV, O.V. IL'ENKO and P.M. CHEGOLIN, Electrical analogues of bending rods. Collection of articles *Electrical analogues of beams and frameworks*. Taganrog 1956.
4. O.V. IL'ENKO and V.I. USYNIN, Electrical analogue EMSS-1 for calculating beams and frameworks. Articles in the present collection.

10

COMPARISON OF THE METHODS
OF BUILDING DYNAMICS
AND THOSE USED IN THE EVALUATION
OF ELECTRICAL CIRCUITS*

P.M. CHEGOLIN

VARIOUS methods of constructional statics are analogous to the theory of electrical networks. Below we show that a similar comparison is valid even in the study of constructional dynamics, namely in determining the frequencies of natural vibration of girders and frames.

Method of Deformations

In [1] it was shown that the equations for determining the free vibrations of a bar (Fig. 1a) and the relationships in a three terminal active network (Fig. 1b) with parameters

$$R = \frac{l}{EJ} (\varphi_a + \psi_a); \ R_0 = -\frac{l}{EJ} \psi_a \ ; \ \gamma = \frac{\Delta y}{l} \qquad (1)$$

are identical. For the bar (Fig. 1a) we have:

$$\left. \begin{array}{l} \varphi_1 = \dfrac{l}{EJ} \varphi_a M_1 + \dfrac{l}{EJ} \psi_a M_2 + \gamma; \\[2mm] -\varphi_2 = \dfrac{l}{EJ} \psi_a M_1 + \dfrac{l}{EJ} \varphi_a M_2 - \gamma; \end{array} \right\} \qquad (2)$$

* Given at the 2nd scientific-technical conference of the TRTI 28th March 1956.

where l — length of the rod;

EJ — rigidity in bending;

$$\varphi_a = \frac{\cotanh\alpha - \cot\alpha}{2\alpha}, \quad \psi_a = \frac{-\cosech\alpha + \cosec\alpha}{2\alpha}; \qquad (3)$$

$$\alpha = Kl = l\sqrt[4]{\left(\frac{\mu\omega^2}{EJ}\right)}, \qquad (4)$$

where μ — mass per unit length;

ω — frequency of free vibrations.

And for the electrical 'T' network (Fig. 1b) we have

$$\varphi_1 = M_1(R + R_0) - M_2 R_0 + \gamma;$$
$$\varphi_2 = M_1 R_0 - M_2(R + R_0) + \gamma.$$

Substituting into these equations the magnitudes of R and R_0 from (1) we obtain equations (2).

We can use the electrical 'T' network of Fig. 1b as an analogue, for studying the free vibrations of structures.

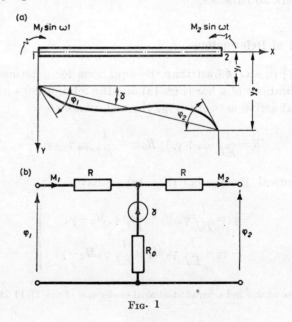

Fig. 1

78

Equations of Three Moments

When calculating the free vibrations of solid bars of finite mass (Fig. 2a) and of variable profile when placed on rigid supports, the following equation of three moments is used:

$$M_{n-1} \frac{l_n}{EJ_n} \psi_n + M_n \left(\frac{l_n}{EJ_n} \varphi_n + \frac{l_{n+1}}{EJ_{n+1}} \varphi_{n+1} \right) +$$
$$+ M_{n+1} \frac{l_{n+1}}{EJ_{n+1}} \psi_{n+1} = 0, \qquad (5)$$

where φ_n and ψ_n — the known frequency functions in using the method of deformations (3);

n — the nth support of the bar.

We shall write the equation for a loop current for the nth mesh of the electrical circuit replacing a solid bar (Fig. 2b):

$$(M_n - M_{n-1}) R_{0, n} + M_n(R_n + R_{n+1}) + (M_n - M_{n+1}) R_{0, n+1} = 0$$

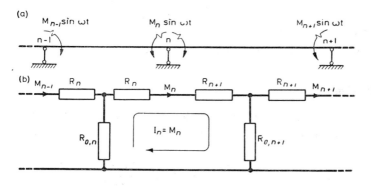

FIG. 2

or

$$-M_{n-1} R_{0, n} + M_n(R_n + R_{0, n} + R_{n+1} + R_{0, n+1}) -$$
$$- M_{n+1} R_{0, n+1} = 0. \qquad (6)$$

For a beam with a distributed mass

$$R_0 = -\frac{l}{EJ} \psi^a \text{ and } R = \frac{l}{EJ} (\varphi_a + \psi_a).$$

Consequently:

$$M_{n-1}\frac{l_{n-1}}{EJ_{n-1}}\,\psi_{n-1}+M_n\left[\frac{l_n}{EJ_n}\,(\varphi_n+\psi_n)-\frac{l_n}{EJ_n}\,\psi_n+\right.$$

$$\left.+\frac{l_{n+1}}{EJ_{n+1}}\,(\varphi_{n+1}+\psi_{n+1})-\frac{l_{n+1}}{EJ_{n+1}}\,\psi_{n+1}\right]+M_{n+1}\frac{l_{n+1}}{EJ_{n+1}}\,\psi_{n+1}=0,$$

from which we finally obtain the equation

$$M_{n-1}\frac{l}{EJ_{n-1}}\,\psi_{n-1}+M_n\left(\frac{l_n}{EJ_n}\,\varphi_n+\frac{l_{n+1}}{EJ_{n+1}}\,\varphi_{n+1}\right)+$$

$$+M_{n+1}\frac{l_{n+1}}{EJ_{n+1}}\,\psi_{n+1}=0, \qquad (7)$$

which is the same as equation (5).

Thus the method of calculating natural frequencies of vibration of solid bars with variable profile, based on the equation of three moments is the analogue of the calculation of mesh currents in electrical networks. Parameters R and R_0 of the electrical circuit are determined in the usual way.

Method of Model

The equation of model relations of vibrations of continuous bars and frames takes the form:

$$K_n=\frac{1}{\psi_n'}\left[(\varphi_{n-1}'+\varphi_n')-\frac{\psi_{n-1}'}{K_{n-1}}\right]. \qquad (8)$$

Equation (8) determines the left model relation of the nth span while

$$K_n=-\frac{M_n}{M_{n-1}}.$$

Reverting to the analogue of the nth span of the bar (Fig. 2a) and taking into account that in the case of free vibrations all the bars are passive (the left and right part of the nth span), we can find the model relation the following way: we write the 2nd law of Kirchhoff for a closed loop circuit (Fig. 3):

$$M_{n-1}(R_\Sigma + R_n + R_{0, n}) - M_n R_{0, n} = 0,$$

on substituting the magnitudes for R and R_0 we obtain:

$$M_{n-1}\left[R_\Sigma + \frac{l_n}{EJ_n}(\varphi_n + \psi_n) - \frac{l_n}{EJ_n}\psi_n\right] + M_n \frac{l_n}{EJ_n}\psi_n = 0,$$

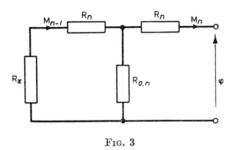

FIG. 3

from which we can determine the model relation:

$$K_n = -\frac{M_n}{M_{n-1}} = \frac{\varphi_n}{\psi_n} + \frac{R_\Sigma}{\psi_n'}, \tag{9}$$

where R_Σ — resistance of the left part of the analogue of the solid bar, that is for all the $n-1$ spans to the left;

$$\varphi_n' = \frac{\varphi_n}{i_n}; \quad \psi_n' = \frac{\psi_n}{i_n};$$

$i_n = EJ_n/l_n$ — the rigidity per unit length.

The method of focuses in the theory of free vibrations of continuous bars is the analogue of calculations of electrical circuits by method of transformations.

To conclude, we must remark that the methods of calculating elastic systems are based on the linear law of Hooke, and the methods of calculating linear electrical circuits on the linear law of Ohm. Therefore, every method of calculation in building mechanics has its counterpart in the laws of electricity.

81

And moreover for elastic systems, using the terms of electrotechnics, it is possible to formulate laws of Kirchhoff for generalized deformations (dislocation, angle of turn) and stresses (forces, moments of force).

The principles of mutual relations are valid to the same degree in elastic systems and electrical circuits. Therefore, we suppose that any linear static or dynamic problem of elastic systems can be formulated in the terms and laws of electricity, that is as an analogue consisting of linear electrical circuits.

References

1. G.Ye. Pukhov and P.M. Chegolin, Comparison of a vibrating rod system with a three-terminal electrical network. Collection of articles *Electrical analogues of beams and frameworks.* Taganrog 1956.

11

ELECTRICAL ANALOGUES
OF VARIABLE PROFILE BEAMS*

G.Ye. Pukhov and P.M. Chegolin

In practical design we often encounter calculations of beams with variable cross-section, variable diameter bars, aircraft wings or frames, comprising elements of variable rigidity. In this paper we shall examine an approximate method using electrical analogues for constructions where an electrical 'T' network is used to represent a bending rod of variable rigidity.

When using an analogue for a beam of variable rigidity we can proceed in two ways.

(1) To reduce the length of the beam of variable profile (rigidity) to the length of a constant, previously chosen, profile, and then to compute the parameters of the symmetrical 'T' network analogue.

(2) To divide the beam of variable profile into sections, over which the rigidity changes according to a linear law and to find the electrical parameters of every section replacing the trapezoids with rectangles and then, finally determining parameters of the equivalent 'T' network analogue for the whole beam.

This method of equivalents replacing the beam is asymmetrical, as can be easily understood from the physical sense of the problem.

The method of reducing variable profile beams to beams of a constant profile, has been well known in the dynamics of

* Given at the 3rd scientific-technical conference of the TRTI 15th March 1957.

buildings [1]. In particular, for a beam with diameters d_2 and d_1 (Fig. 1), the reduced length to diameter d_1 equals:

$$l_r = l_1 \left(1 + \frac{d_2^4}{d_1^4}\right),$$

and for a steel conic roller (Fig. 2) the reduced value of polar inertia with the same length equals:

$$J_r = \frac{3 J_{2p}}{\dfrac{d_2}{d_1}\left(1 + \dfrac{d_2}{d_1} + \dfrac{d_2^2}{d_1^2}\right)}. \tag{1}$$

After reducing the mechanical parameters (lengths, rigidities) it is possible to use a symmetrical 'T' network and determine the natural frequencies of oscillations by either calculating the electrical circuit or constructing an analogue.

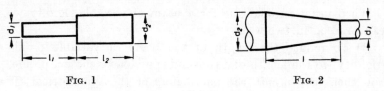

FIG. 1   FIG. 2

As an illustration we shall consider an example. We shall determine critical turns of a staged steel roller (Fig. 1) for which $l_1 = l_2 = 0.2$ m; $d_1 = 6$ cm; $d_2 = 9$ cm. We analyse the bar

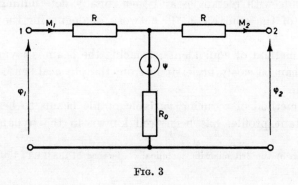

FIG. 3

84

as a beam pin jointed at the ends. The characteristic figures for the bar can be determined from the analogue circuit (Fig. 3), using electromechanical resonance.

We shall apply to this circuit a voltage

$$\varphi_1 = M_1 R_\Sigma, \tag{2}$$

but

$$R_\Sigma = R + R_0 = \frac{l_r}{i} \varphi_{a_1},$$

consequently:

$$\varphi_1 = \frac{l_r}{i} M_1 \varphi_{a_1}. \tag{3}$$

One and the same bending moment M_1 will cause various turns of the end section 1 at various frequencies.

In resonance, the angle of turn will be a maximum and the magnitude $\frac{l_r}{l_j} M_1$ constant. Also the resonance positions will correspond with the maximum of the frequency function. Using the table of numerical values of this function, we write the characteristic numbers

$$\alpha_k = (k+1)\pi$$

for $k = 0,\ 1,\ 2,\ \ldots$.

In the given case

$$\alpha_k = l \sqrt[4]{\left(\frac{\mu_1 \omega_k^2}{i_{p1}} \right)},$$

from where we find:

$$\omega_k = \frac{\alpha_k^2}{l^2} \sqrt{\left(\frac{i_{p1}}{\mu_1} \right)}, \tag{4}$$

where

$$i_{p1} = E J_{p1};$$

$J_{p1} = \pi d_1^4/32$ — polar moment of inertia of the roller with diameter d_1;

μ — mass per unit length;

ω — frequency of oscillations.

We shall find the reduced mechanical parameters:

$$l_r = l_1 \left(1 + \frac{d_2^4}{d_1^4} \right) \approx 1.2 \, \text{m};$$

$$i_{p1} \approx 2.53 \times 10^4 \, \text{kgm}^2;$$

$$\mu_1 \approx 22 \, \text{kg/m}.$$

In accordance with (4), we shall find the frequencies of oscillations:

$$f_0 \approx 44.5 \, \text{sec}^{-1}; \quad f_1 \approx 178 \, \text{sec}^{-1}; \quad f_2 = 400.5 \, \text{sec}^{-1}.$$

If this problem were solved by using the method of dynamics of constructions, we would come to the same results.

We shall examine in some detail the second method of calculating parameters of the circuit for replacing a beam of variable profile.

We shall assume that the rigidity of the beam changes according to the linear law (Fig. 4):

$$i(x) = i_0 - ax, \tag{5}$$

where i_0 — rigidity of the beam at the beginning;

$\quad x$ — abscissa;

$\quad a$ — coefficient of the inclination of the straight line, along which the rigidity of the beam changes;

$i(x)$ — rigidity of the beam at point x.

The coefficient a will relate the rigidity of the initial and final profiles of the beam. In equation (5) when $x = l$, $i = i(l)$, and consequently the equation takes the form:

$$i(l) = -al + i_0, \tag{5a}$$

giving

$$a = \frac{i_0 - i(l)}{l}. \tag{5b}$$

Substituting (5a) into (4) we obtain:

$$i(x) = i_0 - \frac{i_0 - i(l)}{l} x. \tag{6}$$

Now we shall divide the beam of length l into n equal parts. At the end of each section we construct an ordinate to intersect the straight line along which the rigidity changes. Every one of the formed trapezoids will then

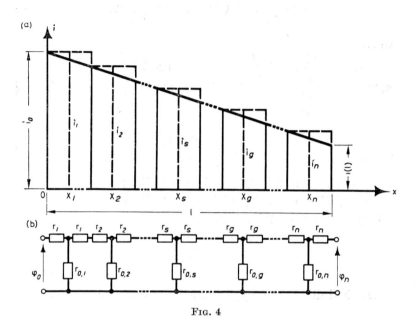

FIG. 4

be replaced by a rectangle with height equal to the height of the ordinate, projected from the middle of the base of every section, the base being equal to the length of the section.

The abscissa at the middle of the sth section will equal.

$$x_s = \frac{l}{n} s - \frac{l}{2n} = \frac{l(2s-1)}{2n}$$

and after substituting X_s into (6) we have:

$$i_s = \frac{i_0(2n-2s+1)+i(l)(2s-1)}{2n} \quad (7)$$

Resistances of the sth electrical analogue are determined as though it was for a beam of constant rigidity i_s and its length was equal to $\dfrac{l}{n}$. In other words we can write:*

$$r_s = \frac{l}{ni_s}(\varphi_s + \psi_s); \quad r_{0,s} = -\frac{l}{ni_s}\psi_s, \tag{8}$$

where

$$\varphi_s = \frac{\cotanh\dfrac{k_s l}{n} - \cot\dfrac{k_s l}{n}}{\dfrac{2k_s l}{n}}; \quad \psi_s = \frac{-\operatorname{cosech}\dfrac{k_s l}{n} + \operatorname{cosec}\dfrac{k_s l}{n}}{2\dfrac{k_s l}{n}}; \tag{9}$$

$$k_s = \sqrt[4]{\left(\frac{\mu_s \omega^2}{i_s}\right)}; \tag{10}$$

μ_s — mass per unit length of the sth section;
i_s — rigidity in bending of the sth section.

Similarly for the gth section

$$k_g = \sqrt[4]{\left(\frac{\mu_g \omega^2}{i_g}\right)}. \tag{11}$$

We shall divide (11) by (10) and solve the result for k_g:

$$k_g = k_s \sqrt[4]{\left(\frac{\mu_g\, i_s}{\mu_s i_g}\right)}. \tag{12}$$

Expression (12) is a formula for reducing the arguments of the hyperbolic-trigonometric functions of the various sections (equation ϱ) to a similar argument for the sth section. This reduction factor is

$$\sqrt[4]{\left(\frac{\mu_g i_s}{\mu_s i_g}\right)}. \tag{13}$$

---

* See equations (3) in the article of P.M. Chegolin "Comparison of the methods of constructional dynamics and those used in the evaluation of electrical circuits" in this collection of articles.

The number of sections into which the beam is divided depends on the required accuracy of the solution and on the inclination to the axis Ox of the straight line giving the change in rigidity. If the inclination is steep it is necessary to divide the beam into many sections.

In the majority of practical cases, the straight line has a small angle of inclination and therefore a division of the span into 2, 3, or 4 sections is sufficient. For every section the reduced rigidity is found and the electrical parameters of the three terminal analogue are determined. Then it is necessary to transform all the 'T' network analogues into one equivalent 'T' network, which would express approximately the whole beam of variable profile. An exception to this is, for example, dynamic calculations of aircraft wings if they are analysed as beams with fact moving rigidity along their length. In this case it is possible to use electrical analogues for equations of bending in finite differences.

To conclude, we shall examine calculations of the parameter for an electrical circuit replacing a beam, of variable rigidity divided into 2 and 4 sections.

We shall first consider the case in which the beam is divided into 2 sections $(n=2)$. For the first section $(s=1)$ and for the second $(s=2)$. From equations (7) and (8) we have:

$$i_1 = \frac{3i_0 + i(l)}{4}, \quad i_2 = \frac{i_0 + 3i(l)}{4}. \tag{14}$$

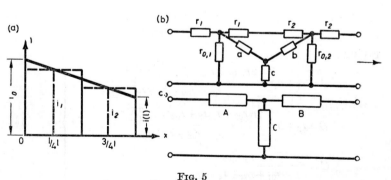

Fig. 5

$$r_1 = \frac{l}{2i_1}\,(\varphi_1 + \psi_1), \quad r_{01} = -\frac{l}{i_1}\,\psi_1; \\
r_2 = \frac{l}{2i_2}\,(\varphi_2 + \psi_2), \quad r_{02} = -\frac{l}{i_2}\,\psi_2. \tag{15}$$

Here

$$\varphi_1 = \frac{\coth\dfrac{k_1 l}{2} - \cot\dfrac{k_1 l}{2}}{k_1 l}; \qquad \psi_1 = \frac{-\operatorname{cosech}\dfrac{k_1 l}{2} + \operatorname{cosec}\dfrac{k_1 l}{2}}{k_1 l};$$

$$\varphi_2 = \frac{\coth\dfrac{k_2 l}{2} - \cot\dfrac{k_2 l}{2}}{k_2 l}; \qquad \psi_2 = \frac{-\operatorname{cosech}\dfrac{k_2 l}{2} + \operatorname{cosec}\dfrac{k_2 l}{2}}{k_2 l}; \tag{16}$$

$$k_1 = \sqrt[4]{\left(\frac{\mu_1 \omega^2}{i_1}\right)}; \qquad k_2 = \sqrt[4]{\left(\frac{\mu_2 \omega^2}{i_2}\right)};$$

μ_1 — mean mass per unit length of the first section;
μ_2 — mean mass per unit length of the second section.

It is possible to find the parameters of the equivalent 'T' network of the beam (Fig. 5a). To do this, we reduce the two connected 'T' networks to an equivalent 'T' network using a delta-star transformation (replacing the impedances r_1, r_2, r_{01} and r_{02} by the impedances a, b and c).

The values of a, b and c are

$$a = \frac{r_{01}(r_1 + r_2)}{r_{01} + r_{02} + r_1 + r_2}; \qquad b = \frac{r_{02}(r_1 + r_2)}{r_{01} + r_{02} + r_1 + r_2};$$

$$c = \frac{r_{01} r_{02}}{r_{01} + r_{02} + r_1 + r_2}; \tag{17}$$

giving

$$A = r_1 + a = \frac{2 r_1 r_{01} + r_{01} r_2 + r_{02} r_1 + r_1^2 + r_1 r_2}{r_{01} + r_{02} + r_1 + r_2};$$

$$B = r_2 + b = \frac{2 r_2 r_{02} + r_{01} r_2 + r_{02} r_1 + r_2^2 + r_1 r_2}{r_{01} + r_{02} + r_1 + r_2}; \tag{18}$$

$$C = c = \frac{r_{01} r_0 r_2}{r_{01} + r_{02} + r_1 + r_2}.$$

Substituting (15) into (17) and rearranging we obtain

$$
\left.
\begin{aligned}
A &= \frac{l}{2i_1} \times \frac{i_1(\varphi_1\varphi_2 - \psi_1\psi_2) + i_2(\varphi_1^2 - \psi_1^2)}{i_2\varphi_1 + i_1\varphi_2}; \\[2mm]
B &= \frac{l}{2i_2} \times \frac{i_2(\varphi_1\varphi_2 - \psi_1\psi_2) + i_1(\varphi_1^2 - \psi_1^2)}{i_2\varphi_1 + i_1\varphi_2}; \\[2mm]
C &= \frac{l}{2} \times \frac{\psi_1\psi_2}{i_2\varphi_1 + i_1\varphi_2},
\end{aligned}
\right\}
\tag{19}
$$

where φ_1, φ_2, ψ_1, ψ_2, i_1 and i_2 are determined from expressions (16) and (14).

In equations (19) the values of resistances A and B, are not equal as the equivalent 'T' network is obviously not symmetrical. The formula for B can be obtained from the formula for A if in the right hand side of the latter the indices 1 and 2 are interchanged.

We shall now analyse a case where the beam is divided into 4 sections ($n=4$). For every one of the sections we first find the reduced rigidities using formula (7):

$$
\left.
\begin{aligned}
i_1 &= \frac{7i_0 + i(l)}{8}; & i_2 &= \frac{5i_0 + 3i(l)}{8}; \\[2mm]
i_3 &= \frac{3i_1 + 5i(l)}{8}; & i_4 &= \frac{i_0 + 7i(l)}{8}.
\end{aligned}
\right\}
\tag{20}
$$

In accordance with formula (8), we find the resistances:

$$
\left.
\begin{aligned}
r_1 &= \frac{l}{4i_1}(\varphi_1 + \psi_1); & r_{01} &= -\frac{l}{4i_1}\,\psi_1; \\[2mm]
r_2 &= \frac{l}{4i_2}(\varphi_2 + \psi_2); & r_{02} &= -\frac{l}{4i_2}\,\psi_2; \\[2mm]
r_3 &= \frac{l}{4i_3}(\varphi_3 + \psi_3); & r_{03} &= -\frac{l}{4i_3}\,\psi_3; \\[2mm]
r_4 &= \frac{l}{4i_4}(\varphi_4 + \psi_4); & r_{04} &= -\frac{l}{4i_4}\,\psi_4,
\end{aligned}
\right\}
\tag{21}
$$

where φ_s and ψ_s $(s = 1, 2, 3, 4)$ are determined from formulae (16). If the linear displacement of the ends of every section of the beam were known then we could determine the e.m.f.'s in the middle arms of the 'T' network from the expression

$$\psi_k = \frac{\Delta y_k}{l/n},$$

and then we would solve it as a case of the distribution of currents (analogue of moments) and voltages (analogue of the angles of deflection) in places where the sections of the beam join. Unfortunately, such a problem cannot be solved without making the simulation very complicated, and moreover a third variable would appear (displacement) in addition to the two other variables (bending moment and the angle of deflection) and the resultant network would have three input magnitudes and three output magnitudes for bending moment, angle of deflection and dislocation respectively. If this problem is to stay as a 'T' network then the solution will have a combined character, a partial solution in the form of calculation or electrical analogue-circuit and a partial solution in the form of an analytical calculation. Such an approach to studying homogeneous (elastic) systems is not convenient and requires the knowledge of an electro-technical engineer as well as a civil engineer.

It is, however, possible in many cases, for instance when determining the frequency of specific oscillations, to confine ourselves merely to determining tension and deformation at the ends of the beam. Then it is necessary to replace the system of four 'T' networks with one equivalent 'T' network. Again using delta-star transformations for the resistances (the various stages in the process are illustrated in (Fig. 6b, c, d, e) we have:

$$a_1 = \frac{r_{01}(r_1 + r_2)}{r_{01} + r_{02} + r_1 + r_2};$$

$$a_2 = \frac{r_{02}(r_1 + r_2)}{r_{01} + r_{02} + r_1 + r_2};$$

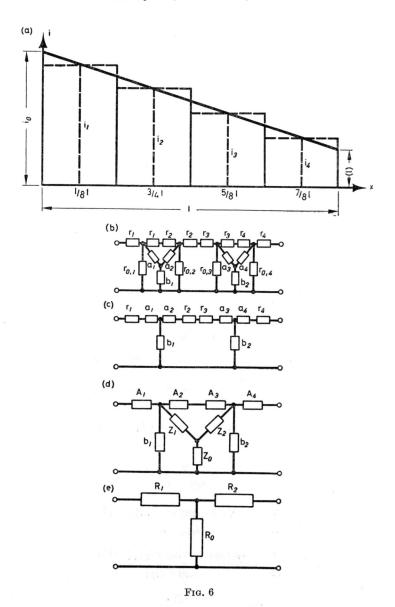

FIG. 6

$$b_1 = \frac{r_{01}r_{02}}{r_{01}+r_{02}+r_1+r_2} \; ;$$

$$a_3 = \frac{r_{03}(r_3+r_4)}{r_{03}+r_{04}+r_3+r_4} \; ;$$

$$a_4 = \frac{r_{04}(r_3+r_4)}{r_{03}+r_{04}+r_3+r_4} \; ;$$

$$b_2 = \frac{r_{03}r_{04}}{r_{03}+r_{04}+r_3+r_4} \; ;$$

$$A_1 = r_1 + a_1; \quad A_2 = a_2 + r_2; \quad A_3 = r_3 + a_3; \quad A_4 = r_4 + a_4;$$

$$Z_1 = \frac{b_1(A_2+A_3)}{b_1+b_2+A_2+A_3} \; ; \quad Z_2 = \frac{b_2(A_2+A_3)}{b_1+b_2+A_2+A_3} \; ;$$

$$Z_0 = \frac{b_1 b_2}{b_1+b_2+A_2+A_3} \; ;$$

$$R_1 = A_1 + Z_1;$$

$$R_2 = A_4 + Z_2;$$

$$R_0 = Z_0.$$

Similarly to (19) for the previous case we have:

$$A_1 = \frac{l}{2i_1} \times \frac{i_1(\varphi_1\varphi_2 - \psi_1\psi_2) + i_2(\varphi_1^2 - \psi_1^2)}{i_2\varphi_1 + i_1\varphi_2} \; ;$$

$$A_2 = \frac{l}{2i_2} \times \frac{i_2(\varphi_1\varphi_2 - \psi_1\psi_2) + i_1(\varphi_2^2 - \psi_2^2)}{i_2\varphi_1 + i_1\varphi_2} \; ;$$

$$b_1 = \frac{l}{2} \times \frac{\psi_1\psi_2}{i_2\varphi_1 + i_1\varphi_2} \; ;$$

$$A_3 = \frac{l}{2i_3} \times \frac{i_3(\varphi_3\varphi_4 - \psi_3\psi_4) + i_4(\varphi_3^2 - \psi_3^2)}{i_4\varphi_3 + i_3\varphi_4} \; ;$$

$$A_4 = \frac{l}{2i_4} \times \frac{i_4(\varphi_3\varphi_4 - \psi_3\psi_4) + i_3(\varphi_4^2 - \psi_4^2)}{i_4\varphi_3 + i_3\varphi_4} \; ;$$

$$b_2 = \frac{l}{2} \times \frac{\psi_3\psi_4}{i_4\varphi_3 + i_3\varphi_4} \; .$$

Thus in this way, rods of variable rigidity can be represented by asymmetrical electrical 'T' networks, the parameters of which are determined from the geometrical and elastic parameters of the rod. To calculate these parameters, it is possible to use numerical tables of frequency functions from the method of deformations.

The conditions of fastening and connecting the rods follow the system of electromechanical analogies, namely: rigid fastening of the left (right) end of the rod ($\varphi_1 = 0$) corresponds to a short circuit of the left (right) terminal of the electrical network and a pin jointed support (the bending moment here equals zero) corresponds to open terminals of the electrical circuit (the current equals zero).

The described method of electrical analogue used in cases of beams with variable profile widens the circle of problems which can be solved by using mathematical analogues.

References

1. S.V. SERENSEN, M.I. TETEL'BAUM and K.I. GRIGOROVSKII, *Dynamic strength in machine construction.* Mashgin. 1945.

12

ELECTRICAL ANALOGUES OF EQUATIONS WITH FINITE DIFFERENCES USED IN CALCULATING BENT RODS*

P.M. CHEGOLIN

General Principles

ELECTRICAL four terminal networks representing bending rods in the static and dynamic sense were obtained on the basis of analysing equations of deformations, that is equations with an incomplete collection of variable values. These equations are deduced by assuming that only a section of the rod system undergoes lateral periodic vibrations. This is why the four terminal network analogue is suitable for analysing only harmonic processes. It cannot be used for polyharmonic vibrations or transitional problems.

For experimental research in polyharmonic lateral vibrations, including problems with percussion loads, and for analysing transitional problems, it is necessary to create an analogue for the differential equation of bending itself which describes the position of any section of the beam at any moment and not relations that would appear to solve this equation on the assumption of harmonic processes.

In this work we shall analyse an electrical circuit replacing a vibrating rod. This scheme is worked out on the basis of electromechanical similarities to a system of equations with

* Given at the 3rd scientific-technical conference of the TRTI 15th March 1957.

finite differences, describing a bending rod. The idea of using this particular scheme came to the author after studying the work of O.T. Roots, *Electrical analogues of cross beams* [1]. The most general approach to the method of electromechanical similarities would be by analysing an elastic system as a mechanism which consists of sample members, serving as a transmission of force and velocity from the sources of mechanical energy to the receivers; such a system is reflected in an electrical circuit, consisting also of sample members chosen as transmissions of voltage and current from the supply of electrical energy to its receiver. The components of the mechanisms would have analogues in the corresponding passive elements of the electrical circuit. A reverse order of the problem would also be adequate.

We shall compare the equations for linear and rotary motion of an elastic system:

$$m\frac{d^2x}{dt^2} + R\frac{dx}{dt} + \frac{1}{s}x = P; \tag{1}$$

$$J\frac{d^2\varphi}{dt^2} + R_\varphi\frac{d\varphi}{dt} + \frac{1}{\sigma}\varphi = M \tag{2}$$

and the equations for electric circuits having inductance L' capacitance C and resistance r all in parallel, and also all in series:

$$L\frac{d^2q}{dt^2} + r\frac{dq}{dt} + \frac{1}{C}q = U; \tag{3}$$

$$C\frac{d^2\Phi}{dt^2} + \frac{1}{r}\times\frac{d\Phi}{dt} + \frac{1}{L}\Phi = I; \tag{4}$$

$$C\frac{d^2U}{dt^2} + \frac{1}{r}\times\frac{dU}{dt} + \frac{1}{L}U = \frac{dI}{dt}, \tag{5}$$

i.e. m, J — mass and inertia of the elastic system;

R, R_φ — coefficients of resistance during linear and rotary motion;

s, σ — flexibility in bending and torsion;

x, φ — linear and angular displacement;

97

q — electric charge;

Φ — magnetic flux;

P, M — amplitudes of applied force and moment;

U, I — magnitude of e.m.f. and current of the supply.

Conditions for equivalence between the elastic and electrical systems must be fulfilled, that is equations describing their behaviour must have corresponding coefficients (elements of the systems) and variables (displacement and force on one

TABLE 1

Parameter	Elastic System		Electrical System	
	Forward motion	Rotating motion	I	II
Constants	m	J	L	C
	R	R_φ	r	$g=\dfrac{1}{r}$
	s	σ	C	L
Variables	x	φ	q	$\Phi;\ U$
	P	M	U	$I;\ \dfrac{dI}{dt}$
Analogies	—	—	$\dfrac{Rt}{m}=\dfrac{r\tau}{L}$	$\dfrac{Rt}{m}=\dfrac{\tau}{rC}$
	—	—	$\dfrac{t^2}{ms}=\dfrac{\tau^2}{LC}$	$\dfrac{t^2}{ms}=\dfrac{\tau^2}{LC}$
	—	—	$\dfrac{t^2}{mx}P=\dfrac{\tau^2}{Lq}U$	$\dfrac{t^2}{ms}P=\dfrac{\tau^2}{C\Phi}I;$ $\dfrac{\tau^2}{CU}\times\dfrac{dI}{dt}$

side, and charge, magnetic flux, voltage and current on the other). For reference the analogous quantities are shown in Table 1. The joining of elements corresponds to connections in the electric circuit, and the sum of forces has its analogue in the 1st system of similarities in the sum of voltages, and in the 2nd system — in the sum of currents or sum of their derivatives.

Numerical magnitudes of the assumed parameters are chosen with the help of similarity criterions. If it were necessary that the processes in the electrical circuit should flow n times faster than the corresponding processes in the elastic system this can be done by choosing correct similarity criterions. So if $n = t/\tau$ for the 2nd system of similarities the parameters take the form

$$\left.\begin{array}{c} \dfrac{Rn}{m} = \dfrac{1}{rC}, \quad \dfrac{n^2}{ms} = \dfrac{1}{LC}, \quad \dfrac{n^2}{mx} P = \dfrac{1}{C\Phi} I; \\[2mm] \dfrac{n^2}{mx} P = \dfrac{1}{CU} \times \dfrac{dI}{dt}. \end{array}\right\} \tag{6}$$

Electrical Analogue of a System of Finite Difference Equations for a Laterally Vibrating Beam

The differential equation of the free lateral vibrations of a suspended bar has the following form:

$$\frac{\partial^2}{\partial x^2}\left(EJ\frac{\partial^2 y}{\partial x^2}\right) = -\mu\frac{\partial^2 y}{\partial t^2}, \tag{7}$$

where μ — the mass per unit length of the bar;
EJ — rigidity in bending.

Equation (7) can be analysed using a sequence of differentiating and multiplying as shown in Table 2, in which are also given the finite difference equations corresponding to the differential equations.

If the equations with finite differences come out of the 2nd system, the analogue circuit would have the form of a five terminal network (Fig. 1). In this case equation (8) expresses

TABLE 2

Differential relations	Equations of finite differences	
$$\dfrac{dy}{dx} = \varphi$$	$$\dfrac{y_{k+1} - y_k}{\Delta x} = \varphi_{k+0.5}$$	(8)
$$-EJ\dfrac{d\varphi}{dx} = M$$	$$\varphi_{k-0.5} - \varphi_{k+0.5} = M_k \dfrac{\Delta x}{EJ}$$	(9)
$$\dfrac{dM}{dx} = P$$	$$\dfrac{M_{k+1} - M_k}{\Delta x} = P_{k+0.5}$$	(10)
$$\dfrac{dP}{dx} = -\mu\dfrac{d^2y}{dt^2}$$	$$P_{k+0.5} - P_{k-0.5} = -\mu\Delta x\dfrac{d^2y}{dt^2}$$	(11)

the relation between the primary and secondary voltages of the transformer, the coefficient of transformation being Δx, and equation (9) expresses Ohm's law for the inductance L_k, of the secondary circuit.

The angles of turn in the accepted scheme of similarities correspond to voltages and moments to the derivatives of currents. Therefore when comparing (9) with the formula for the voltage across an inductance L_k

$$U_L = L\frac{dI}{dt},$$

we have the following expression for the inductance

$$L_k = \frac{\Delta x}{EJ_k}. \tag{12}$$

Equation (10) can be considered as Kirchhoff's law for the sum of derivatives of current at the node $\varphi_{k+0.5}$. The derivative of the current flowing in the secondary winding of the transformer is the product of the derivative of the current in the

100

primary winding $P_k + 0.5$ and the transformation ratio, Δx, i.e. $P_k + 0.5\,\Delta x$.

Equation (11) is Kirchhoff's law for the derivatives of the currents at the node Y_k, where the capacity C_k has the value:

$$C_k = \mu_k \Delta x. \tag{13}$$

Here we have used the similarity between the bending moment and derivative of the current as in equation (11) and the deri-

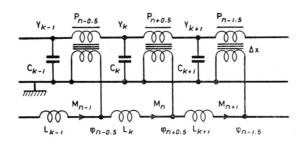

Fig. 1

vative of displacement and its analogue the voltage. Therefore power P and moment M can also be understood as derivatives of currents in corresponding branches. When analysing harmonic processes this condition does not noticeably appear on the oscilloscope, usually used in computing, as there is no change in the character of the curve: cosine curve is transformed into a sine curve and vice versa (i.e. current and derivative only differ in phase). When analysing polyharmonic vibrations and transitional processes it is sufficient to measure voltages y and φ, which reflect the displacement and angle of turn of the analysed profile of the beam and, being measured at several points, they eventually give the shape of vibrations.

Thus, finite difference equations of a bending rod enable us to obtain an electrical analogue circuit, containing transformers and reactive elements.

Electrical Analogues of the Finite Difference Equations Approximation, Twisting and Laterally Vibrating Rod

Differential equations for free twisting and lateral vibrations of a heterogeneous bar can be expressed in the following form:

$$\frac{\partial}{\partial x}\left(GJ_p\frac{\partial \varphi}{\partial x}\right) = -J_m\frac{\partial^2\varphi}{\partial t^2}, \tag{14}$$

$$\frac{\partial}{\partial x}\left(EF\frac{\partial a}{\partial x}\right) = -\mu\frac{\partial^2 a}{\partial t^2}, \tag{15}$$

where φ — angle of twist;
J_m — inertia per unit length;
G — elastic modules for bar in torsion;
J_p — polar inertia of the bar's profile; for round bars (roller);

$J_p = \dfrac{\pi\partial^4}{32}$,   ($\partial$ — diameter of the roller);

GJ_p — rigidity in torsion;
EF — tensile rigidity;
μ — density per unit length of the bar;
F — area of cross section;
a — transverse displacement of the cross bar.

We shall follow the same sequence of operations as in bending vibrations, namely:

(a) we shall imagine the elastic system as a compound and the differential form of equations will be replaced by finite difference equations;

(b) we shall find an electrical circuit-analogue for the compound.

We shall mention that the differential equations (14) and (15) correspond to the loss-less electrical transmission line

$$\frac{\partial^2 u}{\partial x^2} = L_0 C_0\frac{\partial^2 u}{\partial t^2}, \tag{16}$$

where u — voltage at a section, abscissa $\mathbf{x}$, of the line,

L_0, C_0 — inductance and capacitance per unit length of the line.

Comparing the differential equations (14) and (15) for twisting and lateral vibrations of the bar with equation (16) for the length of the line, it is possible to obtain the electrical parameters from the elastic and geometric parameters of the bar.*

To obtain a model with lumped electrical parameters, the differential equation must be replaced by a finite difference equation.

Let us divide the beam into n parts. Then for the kth section we can write the approximate equations:

$$\left.\begin{aligned}
\left(\frac{\partial \varphi}{\partial x}\right)_{k+0.5} &= \frac{\varphi_{k+1} - \varphi_k}{\varDelta x}; \\
\left(\frac{\partial a}{\partial x}\right)_{k+0.5} &= \frac{a_{k+1} - a_k}{\varDelta x}; \ (k = 1, 2, \ldots, n).
\end{aligned}\right\} \quad (17)$$

Using this principle, equations (14) and (15) can be expressed in the following form:

$$\frac{(GJ_0)_{k+0.5}(\varphi_{k+1} - \varphi_k) - (GJ_0)_{k-0.5}(\varphi_k - \varphi_{k-1})}{\varDelta x^2} = J_{mk} \frac{\partial^2 \varphi_k}{\partial t^2}; \quad (18)$$

$$\frac{(EF)_{k+0.5}(a_{k+1} - a_k) - (EF)_{k-0.5}(a_k - a_{k-1})}{\varDelta x^2} = \mu_k \frac{\partial^2 a_k}{\partial t^2}, \quad (19)$$

where $(GJ_p)_{k+0.5}(EF)_{k+0.5}$ also (GJ_p) and (EF) with $x = \dfrac{x_k + x_{k+1}}{2}$,

and $J_{mk}, \ \mu_k - J_m$ also μ with $x = x_k$.

We shall multiply both equations (18) and (19) by $\varDelta x$ and separating the left hand terms, we obtain:

$$\left(\frac{GJ_p}{\varDelta x}\right)_{k+0.5}(\varphi_{k+1} - \varphi_k + \left(\frac{GJ_p}{\varDelta x}\right)_{k-0.5}(\varphi_{k-1} - \varphi_k) =$$
$$= (J_m \varDelta x)_k \frac{\partial^2 \varphi_k}{\partial t^2}; \quad (20)$$

* Such examples of analogues are given and described in (2, 3).

$$\left(\frac{EF}{\Delta x}\right)_{k+0.5}(a_{k+1}-a_k)+\left(\frac{EF}{\Delta x}\right)_{k-0.5}(a_{k-1}-a_k)=$$

$$=(\mu\Delta x)_k\frac{\partial^2 a_k}{\partial t^2}. \tag{21}$$

If the angles of turn and displacements are treated as voltages and their coefficients as derivatives, then equations (20) and (21) can be analysed as Kirchhoff's law for currents at the kth node of the electrical circuit, shown in Fig. 2. The presence of the second derivative of time compels us to analyse every term in (20) and (21) as a derivative of the current. This means that when constructing analogues of harmonic processes the sinusoid of the current will be represented by a cosine curve we might mention that this has no importance if one is solving this problem on an oscilloscope. In the case of analysing polyharmonic and transitional vibrations it is sufficient to measure voltages in order to get the form of the vibrations. A comparison of similar values is shown in Table 3, where parameters of the electric circuit replacing a bar, vibrating laterally are also given.

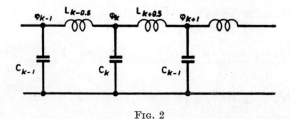

Fig. 2

Table 3

Parameters of the electrical circuit	Vibrations of the bar		
	Torsion	Longitudinal	Lateral
Capacitance	$J_m\Delta x$	$\mu\Delta x$	$\mu\Delta x$
Inductance	$\dfrac{\Delta x}{GJ_p}$	$\dfrac{\Delta x}{EF}$	$\dfrac{\Delta x}{EJ}$

For the $(k+1)$th node, the equations (20) and (21) take the following form:

$$\left(\frac{GJ_p}{\Delta x}\right)_{k+1.5} (\varphi_{k+2}-\varphi_{k+1}) + \left(\frac{GJ_p}{\Delta x}\right)_{k+0.5} (\varphi_k - \varphi_{k+1}) =$$

$$= (J_m\Delta x)_{k+1}\frac{\partial^2 \varphi_{k+1}}{\partial t^2}, \tag{22}$$

$$\left(\frac{EF}{\Delta x}\right)_{k+1.5} (a_{k+2}-a_{k+1}) + \left(\frac{EF}{\Delta x}\right)_{k+0.5} (a_k - a_{k+1}) =$$

$$= (\mu\Delta x)_{k+1}\frac{\partial^2 a_{k+1}}{\partial t^2}. \tag{23}$$

From the analysis of equations (20) and (22), (21) and (23), it follows that the absolute value of the coefficients in these equations are identical if $\varphi_{k+1}-\varphi_k = a_{k+1}-a_k$.

Consequently, the electrical analogy allows the elastic system to be exchanged for the electrical circuit.

We note that in the scheme of Fig.2, it is possible to allow for energy dissipation (irreversible absorption) in an elastic system. It is therefore necessary to connect active resistances in series with capacities.

When deciding on the electrical scheme, it is possible to work on the 1st system of electrical analogies (see Table 1), taking equations (20) and (21) as expressions of Kirchhoff's law for the sum of voltages in the kth loop of the electrical circuit (Fig. 2). Then displacements are taken as charges and their coefficients as impedance of the branches. Then inductances are determined from parameters of the elastic system using the same expressions as in the 2nd system of analogies for calculating capacities, and capacities from those expressions used in the 2nd system for determining inductances. Voltage corresponds to force and current to the velocity of deformation.

Electrical Analogue of a Beam, Vibrating in Bending and Torsion

Previously when working with electrical analogues, we have considered the autonomous aspect of every form of the bar's vibrations. In reality, lateral, longitudinal and torsion vibrations can take place simultaneously giving rise to the problem of determining the resulting form of vibration and finding the natural frequencies of the vibrating beam or frame. In various cases the mutual influence of the various forms of vibration are different. In the vibration theory of an aircraft wing, the combination of bending and torsion vibrations takes the form of a flutter; bending and torsion vibrations have a destructive influence on the blades of a turbo-engine. In frame constructions, used in building, the combination of lateral and longitudinal vibrations is most frequent. The magnitudes of displacement of these and other vibrations may be appreciably affected if we do not allow for longitudinal vibrations; the frequency of natural vibrations may increase up to 10 per cent.

In order to find out to what extent an electrical circuit analogue of torsion vibration can be used for longitudinal vibration, we analyse below analogues of combined torsion-and-bending vibrations and assume that combined bending and longitudinal vibrations can be analysed similarly. The structure of the electrical circuit remains unchanged.

If the distribution of weight on the beam is asymmetric the lateral and torsion vibrations will be described in the following differential equations:

$$\left.\begin{array}{l} \dfrac{\partial^2}{\partial x^2}\left(EJ\,\dfrac{\partial^2 y}{\partial x^2}\right) + m\,\dfrac{\partial^2 y}{\partial t^2} - mb\,\dfrac{\partial^2 \varphi}{\partial t^2} = 0; \\[3mm] + \dfrac{\partial}{\partial x}\left(GJ_p\,\dfrac{\partial \varphi}{\partial x}\right) + J_m\,\dfrac{\partial^2 \varphi}{\partial t^2} + mb\,\dfrac{\partial^2 y}{\partial t^2} = 0, \end{array}\right\} \quad (24)$$

where m — mass per unit length;

b — the distance between the centre of gravity and the axis of rigidity.

106

The meaning of the rest of the magnitudes was explained earlier. Equations (24) differ from equations (7) and (14) because they include items mb expressing the influence of bending on torsion and vice versa.

Rewriting the terms with derivatives of time in (24) in the form:

$$\left.\begin{aligned}
m\frac{\partial^2 y}{\partial t^2} - mb\frac{\partial^2 \varphi}{\partial t^2} &= (m+mb)\frac{\partial^2 y}{\partial t^2} - mb\frac{\partial^2(y-\varphi)}{\partial t^2}\,;\\[2mm]
J_m\frac{\partial^2 \varphi}{\partial t^2} - mb\frac{\partial^2 y}{\partial t^2} &= (J_m-mb)\frac{\partial^2 \varphi}{\partial t^2} - mb\frac{\partial^2(y-\varphi)}{\partial t^2}\,,
\end{aligned}\right\} \quad (25)$$

substituting these expressions in (24) we have:

$$\left.\begin{aligned}
\frac{\partial^2}{\partial x^2}\left(EJ\frac{\partial^2 y}{\partial x^2}\right) + (m+mb)\frac{\partial^2 y}{\partial t^2} - mb\frac{\partial^2(y-\varphi)}{\partial t^2} &= 0\,;\\[2mm]
\frac{\partial}{\partial x}\left(GJ_p\frac{\partial \varphi}{\partial x}\right) + (J_m-mb)\frac{\partial^2 \varphi}{\partial t^2} - mb\frac{\partial^2(y-\varphi)}{\partial t^2} &= 0.
\end{aligned}\right\} \quad (26)$$

Equation (26) differs from (7) and (14) in the common term $mb\ \partial^2(y-\varphi)/\partial t^2$. But the equation of bending (7) and torsion (14) are expressed in finite difference equations and represented by the electrical analogues, shown in Figs. 1 and 2. The structure of the electrical analogue circuit for equation (26) will remain the same as in the previous case if they are bound by a common term $mb\ \partial^2(y-\varphi)/\partial t^2$, which in the 2nd system of analogies is analysed as a derivative of the current in the common connecting branch with capacity $mb\Delta x$ (Fig. 3a). It is characteristic for both analogue-circuits — circuit of bending and circuit of torsion — that they are bound not only by the common term . . . but also because the coefficients m and J_m in the derivatives of time in other terms have the same increments. This condition should be reflected in electrical circuits-analogues by the respective change of the capacity magnitudes.

To write equations with finite difference that would correspond with equation (26) is unnecessary. In Fig. 3 we have the following symbols:

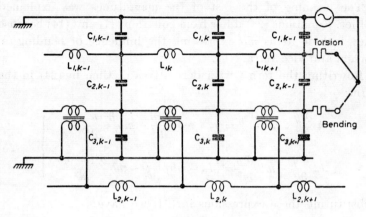

FIG. 3

$$C_{1,\,k}=[\Delta x(J_m+mb)]_k; \qquad C_{2,\,k} \quad mb]_k; \quad C_{3,\,k}=$$
$$=[\Delta x(m+mb)]_k;$$
$$L_{1,\,k}=\left[\frac{\Delta x}{GJ_p}\right]_k \qquad L_{2,\,k}=\left[\frac{\Delta x}{EJ}\right]_k. \qquad \right\} \tag{27}$$

When describing torsion vibrations, the dependence on the given direction of rotation means that the product mb can be positive or negative. In the latter case, elements $C_{2,k}$ are negative and their analogue would be a coil of inductance. As far as the elements $C_{1,k}$ and $C_{2,k}$ are concerned, they can have different signs (plus or minus) depending on the relations in the magnitudes Tm and mb and also m and mb. However, these signs should be conveniently related to the direction of the currents and therefore when deciding on these capacities the necessity of using inductance coils which could cause additional inaccuracies is eliminated.

Some of the elements of the analogue calculated according to formulae (27) for a certain construction could prove far too large and almost impossible in practice. In order to eliminate this drawback we must use coefficients of the scale shown below in the table of variable magnitudes.

Analogues of Conditions for Fastening and Joining the Sections in a Bar System

We shall analyse various basic conditions for fastening and joining bars. Diagrams of these conditions, their analytical descriptions and electrical analogues are shown in Table 4, where in order to simplify the matter the five terminal network is described as a rectangle.

Table 4 is formed on the comparison of similar magnitudes, based on the 2nd system of electromechanical analogies. We can see from Table 4 that the following analogies are used in the modelling of boundary conditions:

(1) rigid fastening with an arbitrary coordinate (y or φ) corresponds in the electrical analogue to short circuited terminals.

(2) free transposition in an arbitrary coordinate corresponds to open circuited terminals.

The end of the bar should correspond in the analogue to one of the nodes of the circuit y_k or $\varphi_{k+5.0}$. For a scheme in Fig. 1 if k is a whole number (the end of the bar should fall into node Y_k) the magnitudes of capacitance and inductance are determined from the formulae:

$$\overline{C}_0 = \mu \frac{y_0 \overline{\Delta x}}{2t_0^2}; \quad \overline{L}_0 = \frac{x_0^4 \overline{\Delta x}}{2y_0 EJ}, \tag{28}$$

because only one half of the length of the first section, $\Delta x/2$, of the beam is used in these elements. Similar conclusions can be drawn for the opposite ends of the beam. If we want to arrange the scheme so that the end of the beam corresponds with the node of the electrical circuit φ, then there will be no coefficient $\frac{1}{2}$ in (28) because it will become a coefficient of transformation $\Delta x{:}2$. Experiments have shown that both ways of placing the end of the bar in node y or node φ do not influence the accuracy of the analogue. Each of them, however, appears to be the analogue of a pinched and pin jointed end of the bar respectively. We shall analyse these features.

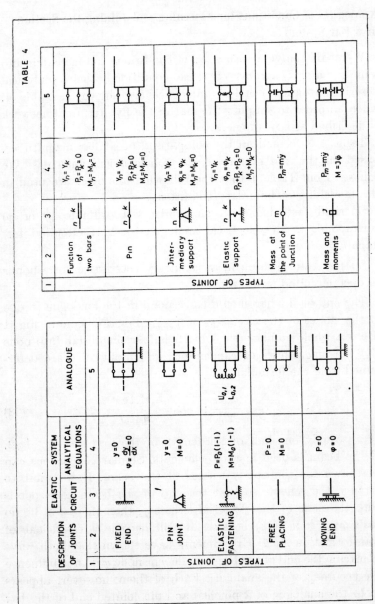

TABLE 4

1	2	3	4	5
TYPES OF JOINTS	Function of two bars	n k	$y_n = y_k$ $P_n = P_k = 0$ $M_n = M_k = 0$	
	Pin	n k	$y_n = y_k$ $P_n + P_k = 0$ $M_n = M_k = 0$	
	Inter-mediary support	n k	$y_n = y_k$ $\varphi_n = \varphi_k$ $M_n = M_k = 0$	
	Elastic support	n k	$y_n = y_k$ $\varphi_n = \varphi_k$ $P_n + P_k + P_C = 0$ $M_n + M_k = 0$	
	Mass at the point of Junction	m	$P_m = m\ddot{y}$	
	Mass and moments	J	$P_m = m\ddot{y}$ $M = J\ddot{\varphi}$	

1	2	3	4	5
	DESCRIPTION OF JOINTS	ELASTIC SYSTEM		ANALOGUE
		CIRCUIT	ANALYTICAL EQUATIONS	
TYPES OF JOINTS	FIXED END		$y = 0$ $\varphi = \dfrac{dy}{dx} = 0$	
	PIN JOINT		$y = 0$ $M = 0$	
	ELASTIC FASTENING		$P = P_0(l-t)$ $M = M_0(l-t)$	$U_{0,1}$ $L_{0,2}$
	FREE PLACING		$P = 0$ $M = 0$	
	MOVING END		$P = 0$ $\varphi = 0$	

110

(a) *Pinched bar end placed at node y*

At the fastened end of the beam $y_0 = 0$ and $\varphi_0 = 0$. Shall we say that it is the left end, the analogue of which is shown in Fig. 4a. From Fig. 4b it follows that condenser C (shown as dotted line) should be withdrawn from the circuit as each of its ends have zero potential (are earthed).

(b) *Pinched bar end placed at node φ*

Let us say that the pinched end coincides with the node Fig. 5a. Potential $\varphi_{0.5}$ (analogue of the angle of turn) at point $x = \frac{1}{2}$ equals zero and consequently, the secondary coil of the first transformer is earthed (Fig. 5b); the middle point of the primary coil should also be earthed because its coefficients of transformations are, as was said before, equal to $\Delta x/2$.

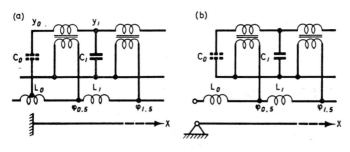

Fɪɢ. 4

In the physical sense, flexure y_1 in the middle of the first element, if the beam is divided into a sufficient number of sections, is not too big and therefore potential of node y_1 is also small. To simplify the scheme, the first transformer can be omitted, calculating the displacement y_2 in the middle of the first element as equal to zero. Under these circumstances, the condenser C_1 is also superfluous. (It is shown in Fig. 5a as a dotted line.)

111

This way the number of elements in the electrical analogue is reduced to two. We shall note that a similar simplification can be made in the previous case if we consider the angle of turn of the middle section of the first element of the beam equal to zero.

The possibility of such a simplification depends on the number of divisions, that is on the number of sections, into which the beam is broken.

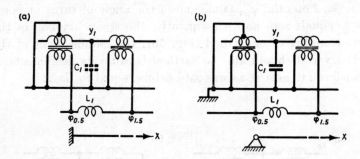

FIG. 5

(c) *Pin jointed beam end placed at node y* (Fig. 4b)

Conditions of potential y_0 are the same as in (a) and similarly condenser C can be withdrawn from the circuit. Boundary conditions for the angle of turn φ (analogue-voltage) do not come into the case of a pin jointed end.

(d) *Pin jointed beam placed at node φ* (Fig. 5b)

Let us say that the pin jointed end coincides with node $\varphi_{0.5}$. The middle point of the primary coil of the transformer should be earthed because the coefficient of transformation equals $\Delta x/2$. The moment at the point $x=0.5$ equals zero ($M_0=0$), therefore the inductive part of the circuit on the left of $\varphi_{0.5}$ is broken and in the vertical branch, corresponding with point $x=0.5$ the current is equal to M_1.

These features should be taken as simplifications (small number of elements) of the electrical analogue scheme. However, there are no difficulties in fulfilling boundary conditions as shown in Table 4. When deciding on the analogue, we are governed by the required order of placing the ends: all ends should coincide either with nodes y or with nodes φ. There can be no combination of these two alternatives for one beam, as in such a case the calculation of elements and coefficients would become very difficult because the beam sections would be expressed in fractions.

The Advantages and Disadvantages of a Transformer Circuit-analogue

The great advantage of a transformer analogue of a vibrating beam is that it enables us to use it for studying a large number of problems of dynamics. The main problems are:

(1) Research in free and forced harmonic vibrations. Here external forces are represented in the analogue as currents in y nodes of the circuit, and bending moments as currents in φ nodes of the circuit with locations corresponding to the loaded profile of the beam. Voltages in the coils of the transformer reflects linear deformations and voltages in nodes — angles of turn of the beam's profile; this way we can obtain the more accurate coordinates of the line of influence, angles of turn and stresses, the bigger the number of divisions of the beam.

(2) Analysis of percussion load influence and polyharmonic vibrations. To illustrate periodic percussions by way of the electrical circuit we must use a pulse generator or a more simple cyclic breaker which, by changing the speed of rotation, can change the frequency of the percussion loads. The study of polyharmonic vibrations involves the use of a special generator of current or voltage such as a photo-electric transducer constructed by I.M. Tetel'baum [2].

(3) Study of transitory processes in beams of various geometric and elastic parameters.

113

(4) Determination of deformations and stresses along the beam when statically loaded. The above described circuit analogue (Fig. 1), with the exclusion of condensers, becomes O.T. Roots' circuit used as the analogue of statically loaded cross beams.

All these problems can be solved in cases of homogeneous beams, as well as beams of variable profile with arbitrary complexity, if the law of changing rigidity and load distribution is given.

The greatest disadvantages of the finite difference analogy are:

(1) More complicated scheme, as far as the form and structure is concerned, than a three terminal network; this disadvantage cannot be overcome.

(2) Large inaccuracies (7–8 per cent) in results; these inaccuracies are caused in the first place by the exchange of differential relations for finite difference expressions and also by the errors in the analogue elements. The optimum number of sections into which the beam should be divided can be calculated by experiment or by calculations. The experiments have shown that it is necessary to divide a homogeneous beam into 3, 4–5 sections; for bar systems it is sufficient to have 3 sections on one span. In any case, the inaccuracy of the result can be calculated beforehand and depends on the number of sections into which the span is divided.

The elements of inductance and capacity can be selected with the accuracy of ±1 per cent and consequently, in order to establish beforehand the sufficient accuracy of the result. These parameters depend on the frequency, and therefore the analogue must be used in a wide range of frequencies. The transformers and their weaknesses can also effect the accuracy of the results. The most suitable transformers are those with toroid core.

(3) The distributed forces should be reduced to concentrated forces, and the number should not exceed the general number of sections forming the analogue of the beam.

Design of Analogue Elements of a Homogeneous Beam and of a Beam with Variable Profile

The magnitudes of inductance L_k and capacitance C_k, calculated from formulae (12) and (13), can be too big to be used in practice. Coefficient of transformation and frequency of vibration can also be suitable for an analogue.

In order to be able to design an electrical analogue usable in practice, it is necessary to observe the criteria of similarity which can usually be established from the natural equations and equations of the analogue. If we, however, have no equations to describe the process in the electrical circuit, we proceed in the following way. Element of capacity $C_k = \mu_k \varDelta x$ is formally determined as a product of coefficient μ in the derivative of time necessary for a finite increase in length of the beam $\varDelta x$, and element of inductivity $L_k = \varDelta K/(EJ)k$ as a relation of the finite increment of the beam length $\varDelta x$ to the coefficient $(EJ)k$ of the derivative of the coordinate. Consequently, if the variable values are expressed as basic and non-dimensional, as is the case in the theory similarity, and if C_k and L_k are found according to the characteristic, then it is not necessary to write electrical equations.

In accordance with this method we take the basic magnitudes x_0, y_0, and t_0. Then:

$$x = x_0 \bar{x}; \quad y = y_0 \bar{y}; \quad t = t_0 \bar{t}, \tag{29}$$

where $\bar{x}$, $\bar{y}$, $\bar{t}$ — non dimensional coordinates and time. Substituting these values (29) into equations (7) we obtain:

$$EJ \frac{y_0}{x_0^4} \frac{\mathrm{d}^4 \bar{y}}{\mathrm{d}\bar{x}^4} = -\mu \frac{y_0}{t_0^2} \frac{\mathrm{d}^2 \bar{y}}{\mathrm{d}\bar{t}^2}. \tag{30}$$

Consequently:

$$\bar{L} = \frac{\varDelta x}{EJ \dfrac{y_0}{x_0^4}}; \quad \bar{C} = \varDelta x \mu \frac{y_0}{t_0^2} \tag{31}$$

115

or

$$\overline{L} = \frac{x_0^4 \Delta \overline{x}}{y_0 EJ}; \quad \overline{C} = \mu \frac{y_0 \Delta \overline{x}}{t_0^2}. \tag{31a}$$

The basic values x_0, y_0, t_0 can be selected in such a way that $\overline{L}$ and $\overline{C}$ would be acceptable in practice and the electrical analogue could be constructed of transformers with the number of coils equal to:

$$\Delta \overline{x} = \frac{l}{x_0 N}. \tag{32}$$

To form an analogue of a beam it is necessary to divide it into a number of sections of which every one would correspond with the electrical circuit group. Such a group includes:

(1) transformer with a coefficient of transformation $\Delta \overline{x}$;

(2) coil of self-inductance $\overline{L}$ and

(3) condenser $\overline{C}$.

Depending on the required accuracy, the number of electrical groups for one and the same beam can vary and therefore, parameters $\overline{L}$ and $\overline{C}$ should be variable (variable inductance or a number of inductances, condenser of a variable capacity or a loss of condensers). For the same reason, it is necessary to be able to change the coefficient of transformation Δx, which can be done by sectionalizing the secondary coil of the transformer.

If the rigidity and mass per unit length of the beam change arbitrarily, it is possible to disregard boundaries of the beam and divide it into equal sections. The given graph of changing rigidity is broken into sections with linear change of rigidity along the length of the beam. Then equations (31) and (32) take the following form:

$$\overline{L}_k = \frac{x_0^4 \Delta \overline{x}_k}{y_0 (EJ)_{k+0.5}}; \quad \overline{C}_k = \frac{y_0}{t_0^2} \mu_{k+0.5} \Delta \overline{x}_k, \; \Delta \overline{x}_k = \frac{\Delta x_k}{x_0}, \tag{33}$$

where Δx_k — actual length of the section with the given rigidity and mass per unit length;

$(EJ)_{k+0.5}$ — rigidity given for kth section;

$\mu_{k+0.5} = \dfrac{\mu_k + \mu_{k+1}}{2}$ — linear unit of mass of kth section;

$x_0,\ y_0,\ t_0$ — basic magnitudes.

Check of the Analogue Circuit

In order to check the basic method of analogues of finite difference equations and to test the quality of the transformer analogue, we have analysed vibrations of a homogeneous beam with various boundary conditions and the results obtained were compared with similar ones from building mechanics. The question of the optimal number of sections necessary for the use of an analogue was also explained.

The spectrum of frequencies of a homogeneous beam is determined in the following expression

$$f_n = \frac{k_n^2}{2\pi} \sqrt{\left(\frac{EJ}{\mu}\right)}, \qquad (34)$$

where k_n — roots of a partial equation. The meaning of these for various forms of fixing the ends is well known [4].

Substituting EJ and μ from (31) into (34) and taking into account that

$$l = N x_0 \overline{\Delta x},$$

$$\overline{\Delta x} = \sqrt{\left(\frac{L_1}{L_2}\right)},$$

where L_1 — magnetizing inductance;

L_2 — leakage inductance of the transformer, we find:

$$f_n = \frac{\alpha_n^2}{2\pi N^2 t_0} \sqrt{\left(\frac{L^2}{L_1} \cdot \frac{1}{\overline{L}\ \overline{C}}\right)}. \qquad (35)$$

In (35) for resonant frequencies in a transformer analogue circuit, the factor $\sqrt{(L_2/L_1)}$ reflects the influence of the transformer on these frequencies. If the beam is divided into a definite number of sections N and consequently, in a general case, there would be the same number of groups, then the resonant frequencies would be defined only as the relation between the constant of time t_0 and the partial factor $\sqrt{(1/LC)}$. Therefore, if there is a voltage generator with a large number of frequencies in the analogue, it is possible to use a wide range of frequency values $\overline{L}$ and $\overline{C}$.

The resonant properties of the analogue-circuit can be defined by changing the voltage of the supply. For practical purposes it is convenient to use a sound generator type ZG-10 or ZG-2 as a generator of variable e.m.f.

(a) *Console*

A transformer analogue of a console beam (homogeneous) was constructed from 6, 8 and 10 groups, corresponding to the divisions of the beam. A normal form of vibrations was analysed. The number of sections into which the beam was divided did not effect in practice the magnitude of frequency of the 1st and 2nd form of vibrations. At larger frequencies, leakage of the transformer occurred and the magnetizing inductance changed. Unfortunately, we did not use transformers with toroid cores and therefore were unable to study their suitability for the analogue. But we imagine they would be most effective because of their small leakage inductance.

A console beam also enabled us to analyse conditions for analogues of boundary conditions: pinching and free placing.

Parameters of the analogue L and C varied over a wide range which influenced the scale of time. The measurements of resonant frequencies of the analogue circuit were done with the help of an oscillograph EO-7 and the voltage in a 2Ω wire resistance. The latter was connected to one of the branches of the circuit. Resonant frequencies correspond with minimum current in the circuit, or, which means the same thing, maximum resistances. The character of the minimum current could be observed on the oscillograph's curve with accuracy to 1 per cent. Experiments were made with five types of transformers, which varied in the coefficient of magnetizing to leakage reactance ratio and in the coefficient of transformation. We came to the conclusion that the first one of these coefficients should be higher and near 1.

(b) *Beam with one fixed and one pin jointed end*

With the help of an electrical analogue we have defined natural frequencies for a beam with the following parameters:

$$\mu = 100 \text{ kg/m}; \quad l = 8 \text{ m}; \quad EJ = 2 \times 10^6 \text{ kgm}^2.$$

If $N = 8$; $\Delta x = 1$; $t_0 = 100$ and $y_0 = 10^{-6}$ parameters of a dummy analogue equal:

$$C = 1 \ \mu f \qquad L = 0.5 \text{ gm}.$$

The sound generator provided voltage 12V. It was possible to change smoothly the frequency of the generated voltage and its magnitude was kept unchanged. Altering the frequencies, we observe the oscillogram of voltage, measured resistance and when the minimum appears, we read the frequency on ZG-10.

In order to make the start of the minima more prominent it is better to remove the horizontal display on the oscillograph and then a vertical line will appear on the screen and the minimum would be apparent.

The combination of natural frequencies of symmetrical and asymmetrical vibrations obtained on the analogue were 4,300 and 13,700.

Taking into account the scale of time $t_0 = 100$ the actual frequencies of the vibrating beam were 43 sec^{-1} and 137 sec^{-1}. The error in determining natural frequencies of vibration on the analogue did not exceed 7 per cent.

References

1. O.T. ROOTS, *Electrical analogues of intersecting beams.* Publishing House of the Tomsk Polytechnical Institute. Tomsk. 1952.
2. I.M. TETEL'BAUM, *Electrical analogues of torsional vibrations of piston-engines rollers.* Oborongiz. 1945,
3. G.Yn. PUKHOV, On the question of electrical analogues of transitional movements of rods. *Transactions of the Dnepropetrovsk Institute of Railway Transport Engineers.* Fasc. 25. 1956.
4. E.V. ANAN'EV, *Manual of the calculations for the natural vibrations of the electric systems.* Gostekhizdat. 1946.

13

ON THE ELECTRICAL ANALOGUE
OF A BENT ROD
USED BY CORBETT AND CALVERT

G.YE. PUKHOV

THE electrical circuit-analogue of a bending rod, designed by Corbett and Calvert, is similar to others constructed in the U.S.S.R. [2, 3, 4, 5] and Chinese Peoples Republic [6].

As we shall explain later, the circuit of Corbett and Calvert is theoretically incorrect and can therefore be used only in very simple cases. (For example: single bar, open bar system, plane beam).

The observations stated below prove this point.

First Observation

For bars, loaded externally with bending moments and forces, Corbett and Calvert used an electrical circuit similar to our scheme shown in Fig. 1.

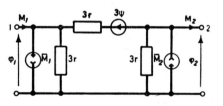

FIG. 1. Electrical circuit of Corbett and Calvert

FIG. 2. Positive directions of bending moments and angles of turn of the bar in bending according to Pukhov, Corbett and Calvert

121

Angles of turn φ_1, φ_2, ψ of the bar in Fig. 2, where positive directions of the moments and their angles of turn are shown, correspond to electrical voltages in Fig. 1. (The same symbols are used in both drawings). The positive direction in Fig. 2, chosen by Corbett and Calvert is clock-wise, whereas Pukhov's scheme is anti-clockwise. The source of currents M_1 and M_2 correspond to bending moments caused by the natural load if the ends are fastened rigidly and if $\psi = 0$. Parameter $r = l/6$ EJ.

We can easily see that the analogue circuit in Fig. 1 does not correspond with the equations:

$$M_1 = \frac{2EJ}{l}(2\varphi_1 + \varphi_2 - 3\psi) + \overline{M}_1; \tag{1}$$

$$M_2 = \frac{2EJ}{l}(\varphi_1 + 2\varphi_2 - 3\psi) + \overline{M}_2, \tag{2}$$

or which it was constructed.

As an example we shall analyse an unloaded pin jointed rod with fixed ends. To point 1 of this rod we apply a bending moment; the following conditions are observed $\overline{M}_1 = 0$, $\overline{M}_2 = 0$, $M_2 = 0$ and $\psi = 0$. From equations (1) and (2) we find that $\varphi_2 = -0.5\ \varphi_1$. In the case of a single rod it would be possible to arrive at a correct result by changing the positive direction of the output voltage. When modelling a rod system, composed of rods (beams) connected in a straight line, it is necessary to assume various positive directions of voltages in odd and even rods in the three terminal analogue which is also recommended by Corbett and Calvert. However, for more complex systems that Corbett and Calvert have in mind, such an arbitrary selection of positive directions of currents and voltages would lead to inaccurate results, as the modelling circuit does not fully correspond with the bending rod. This observation concerns mainly frame constructions, which will be mentioned again.

Full agreement between the equations of a bending rod and the equations of the electrical model circuit is found in the electrical circuits shown in Figs. 3–11 and can be proved by weiting the equations of Kirchhoff for these circuits.

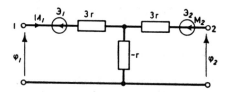

FIG. 3. First electrical circuit of Pukhov

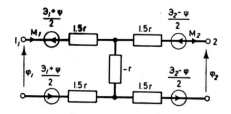

FIG. 4. Second electrical circuit of Pukhov

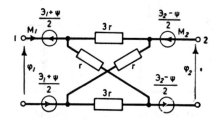

FIG. 5. First electrical circuit of Il'enko

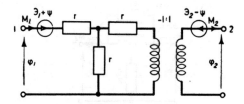

FIG. 6. Second electrical circuit of Il'enko

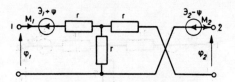

FIG. 7. First electrical circuit of Pukhov,
Il'enko and Chegolin

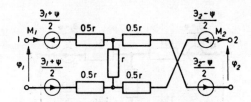

FIG. 8. Second electrical circuit of Pukhov,
Il'enko and Chegolin

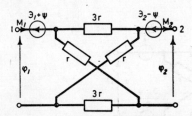

FIG. 9. First electrical circuit of
Li-Tszya-Syun

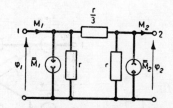

FIG. 10. Second electrical
circuit of Li-Tszya-Syun

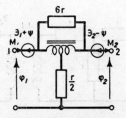

FIG. 11. Third electrical
circuit of Li-Tszya-Syun

124

Analysing Figs. 3–11 we can see that in order to achieve correct correspondence between the bending moments and angles of turn of a bending rod and the currents and voltages of the electrical analogue, the latter must include negative resistance, or a transformer, or crossed outputs.

At the same time we must note that circuits with transformers are less convenient than the others in practice as it is very difficult to construct a transformer without leakage.

Second Observation

Corbett and Calvert advise the use of the circuit as shown in Fig. 1 not only for modelling single rods but also for electrical analogues of complex frame systems, with closed loops for asymmetric frames, or in asymmetric application of loads.

We shall prove that the circuit according to Fig. 1 cannot as a rule give correct results.

In order to give correct results the input currents of all modelling four terminal networks would have to be equal in magnitude. Apart from this, it is known from the theory of electrical circuits [7, 8] that this is only possible with so-called symmetrical connections. To obtain symmetrical connections, the four terminal networks would have to be symmetrical in relation to the horizontal axis, or they would have to have transformers.

To preserve these conditions we can conclude that any of the circuits shown in Figs. 4, 5, 6 or 8 would be suitable. The circuit shown in Fig. 10 (Li-Tszya-Syun's scheme) is suitable for this purpose and can be transformed (replacing the angle $3_1 + \psi$ and $3_2 - \psi$ by half the value in the horizontal arms) into the bridge circuit of Fig. 5 given by O.V. Il'enko.

Our experiments have shown that the circuit of Corbett and Calvert does not provide accurate results.

Third Observation

Corbett and Calvert designed a circuit [1] analogue for modelling partial rod systems as in Fig. 12. The authors analyse a frame shown in Fig. 13; the rod 1–2 is modelled by the circuit in Fig. 12 and the others by the circuit of Fig. 1.

Even in this case the electrical circuit modelling the frame will not provide accurate results as the distribution of electrical currents and voltages does not correspond with the distribution of bending moments and angles of turn at the frame's joints.

Correct results could be obtained by a slightly different combination of the scheme, namely: rods of a closed outline (4–5, 5–8, 8–7, 4–7) should be modelled by the circuits in Fig. 12 and the remaining ones — by the circuit of Fig. 1. Apart from this the positive directions of moments and angles of turn would correspond with the directions of currents and voltages.

Conclusion

Corbett and Calvert apparently did not check their analogues of bending rods with experimental observations. In any case there is no experimental data in their work [1] with the exception of the statement that the count of voltages in the electrical circuit could reach the speed of 300–400 in one hour.

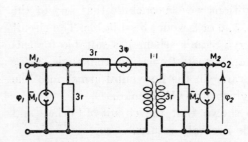

FIG. 12. Electrical circuit of Corbett and Calvert used as an analogue of frameworks as seen in Fig. 13

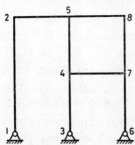

FIG. 13. Circuit of the framework analysed by Corbett and Calvert

As we have already explained, the electrical analogues of Corbett and Calvert (Figs. 1 and 12) cannot be used either for electrical modelling of complex frame systems, or for electro-technical calculations of such frames.

The work of Corbett and Calvert was the first attempt at solving the problems of building mechanics using three terminal electrical networks.

References

1. J.P. CORBETT and I.E. CALVERT. An analogue computer for indeterminate mechanical structures. *Proceedings of the National Electronic Conference,* 6. 1950.
2. G.YE. PUKHOV. *On the question of applying the methods of electrical analogues to the problem of bending plane rod systems.* 2. Publishing House of the Tomsk Polytechnical Institute. 1952.
3. G.YE. PUKHOV. Application of electrical circuits to the problem of bending plane rod systems. *Electricity.* No. 9. 1953.
4. O.V. IL'ENKO. *On the question of electrical analogues of rod systems and the results of some experiments.* Taganrog Radiotechnical Institute. Second scientific-technical conference 26 – 30 March 1956. Reports, Taganrog. 1956.
5. Collection of articles *Electrical analogues of beams and frameworks.* Taganrog, 1956.
6. LI-TSZYA-SYUN'. *Electrical analogues used to solve problems of bending plane rod systems.* Transactions of the Khabrinsk Polytechnical Institute. (In Chinese with summary in Russian). No. 10. 1956.
7. E.V. ZELYAKH. *Principles of the general theory of electrical circuits.* Publishing House of the Academy of Sciences of the U.S.S.R. 1951.
8. G.YE. PUKHOV. Geometrical theory of circuits, consisting of four-pole. *Scientific records of L'vov Polytechnical Institute.* Fasc. 10. L'vov. 1949.

14

ELECTRICAL ANALOGUES
OF BEAMS AND FRAMES, BUILT
ON A FLAT ELASTIC FOUNDATION
AND FIRM SUPPORTS

G.YE. PUKHOV and O.V. IL'ENKO

THE complex problem of electrical modelling of a beam with continuous elastic foundation (Fig. 1a) was solved by L.A.

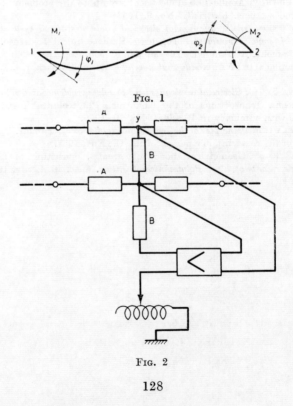

FIG. 1

FIG. 2

Goflin, with the help of the analogue shown in Fig. 2. Every span of the beam is modelled by one ninth of such a scheme all connected into a network.

We shall show further that it is possible to obtain a more simple analogue in the form of a network similar to the four terminal active networks used in solving other problems of building mechanics [3, 4, 5].

Analogue of a Single Beam

We shall use the formulae used in the method of initial parameters [2, 5]

$$\left. \begin{aligned} y_2 &= Ay_1 + LB\varphi_1 - \frac{L^2C}{EJ}M_1 - \frac{L^3D}{EJ}Q_1 + \overline{y}; \\ \varphi_2 &= A\varphi_1 - \frac{LB}{EJ}\varphi_1 - \frac{L^2C}{EJ}Q_1 - \frac{AD}{L}y_1 + \overline{\varphi}; \\ M_2 &= AM_1 + LBQ_1 + k_0L^2Cy_1 + k_0L^3D\varphi_1 + \overline{M}, \end{aligned} \right\} \quad (1)$$

where A, B, C, D — hyperbolic-trigonometric functions determined according to tables with abscissa equal to $\xi = l/L$;

l — length of the rod;

L — characteristic of the rod and the foundation given by:

$$L = \sqrt{\left(\frac{4EJ}{k_0}\right)},$$

k_0 being the rigidity of the foundation.

Magnitudes $\overline{y}, \overline{\varphi}, M$, represent the dislocation, the angle of turn and the bending moment on the right side of the rod caused by the span load.

In the case of rigid unshifting supports it is possible to assume $y_1 = y_2 = 0$, and after excluding the intersecting force Q_1, we obtain the following equations:

G.Ye. Pukhov and O.V. Il'enko

$$\varphi_1 = \frac{l}{EJ} \times \frac{S}{\xi G} M_1 + \frac{l}{EJ} \times \frac{D}{\xi G} M_2 + \varphi_1;$$
$$-\varphi_2 = \frac{l}{EJ} \times \frac{D}{\xi G} M_1 - \frac{l}{EJ} \times \frac{S}{\xi G} M_2 + \varphi_2, \qquad (2)$$

and also

$$M_1 = \frac{EJ}{l} \times \frac{\xi GS}{S^2 + D^2} \varphi_1 + \frac{EJ}{l} \times \frac{\xi GD}{S^2 + D^2} \varphi_2 + \overline{M}_1;$$
$$M_2 = \frac{EJ}{l} \times \frac{\xi GD}{S^2 + D^2} \varphi_1 + \frac{EJ}{l} \times \frac{\xi GS}{S^2 + D^2} \varphi_2 + \overline{M}_2. \qquad (3)$$

In equations (2) we use the following symbols:

$$S = CB - AD; \quad G = B^2 + 4D^2, \qquad (4)$$

φ_1 and φ_2 — angles of turn of the pin-jointed rod caused by the span load.

Equations (3) are obtained from (2) if we solve them in relation to M_1 and M_2. If, (according to [3]) we treat the angles of turn φ as electrical voltages and the bending moments M as currents, then with the help of Kirchhoff's equations we can prove that equations (2) and (3) correspond to the three or four terminal analogues shown in Figs. 3a and 4 respectively.

Parameters* R_k and g_k are determined from the expressions:

$$R_1 = R_2 = \frac{l}{EJ} \times \frac{S+D}{\xi G}; \quad R_0 = -\frac{l}{EJ} \times \frac{D}{\xi G}; \qquad (5)$$

$$g_1 = g_2 = \frac{EJ}{l} \times \frac{\xi(S-D)}{S^2 + SD + D^2}; \quad g_0 = \frac{EJ}{l} \times \frac{\xi D}{S^2 + SD + D^2}. \qquad (6)$$

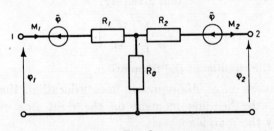

Fig. 3

* The passive parameters of the circuit are: resistances, capacitors and inductances. Active parameters are: sources of current and voltages.

We must note that if $k_0 = 0$ (two supports and elastic foundation):

$$R_1 = R_2 = \frac{l}{2EJ} = 3r; \quad r = \frac{l}{6EJ};$$

$$R_0 = -\frac{l}{6EJ} = -r, \tag{7}$$

we have the parameters characterizing the analogue-circuit of a simply transversally bent rod [3].

The parameters R_k and g_k for different values of the abscissa $\xi = l/L$ can have different signs.

The circuits shown in Figs. 3 and 4 can be designed more easily if their parameters are realized using reactive elements of different signs; that is capacitors and inductances. However, both circuits can be realized using passive elements of the same sign. We shall analyse this possibility by considering the scheme shown in Fig. 3.

Let us say that $R = R_1 = R_2 > 0$ and $R_0 < 0$.

In this case the scheme in Fig. 3 can be transformed into a similar one but comprised of positive resistances $R' = R_1' = R_2'$ and R_0' (Fig. 5a).

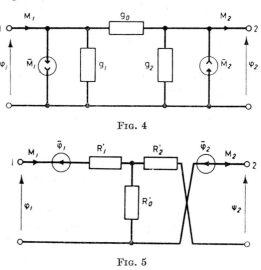

Fig. 4

Fig. 5

131

The action of negative resistance will be expressed in crossing the output elements as was done in the case [4] of an analogue modelling a simply transversally bent rod.

The circuits in Figs. 3a and 5 will be equivalents in relation to input and output if the following conditions are fulfilled:

$$R + R_0 = R_0' + R_0'; \quad R + \frac{R R_0}{R + R_0} = R' + \frac{R' R_0'}{R' + R_0'}. \tag{8}$$

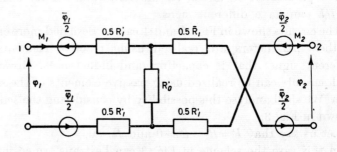

Fig. 6

Hence, solving the quadratic equation, we obtain:

$$R_{\mathrm{I}}' = \left\{ \begin{array}{l} R + 2 R_0 \\ R - R_0 \end{array} \right. \text{ and } R_0' = \left\{ \begin{array}{l} - R_0; \\ 2 R_0. \end{array} \right\} \tag{9}$$

Thus the circuit of Fig. 5 can be realized using positive resistances only, provided that

$$\left. \begin{array}{l} R' = R_1' = R_2' = R + 2 R_0; \\ R_0' = - R_0. \end{array} \right\} \tag{10}$$

When using d.c. R' and R_0' appear to be non-reactive resistances and using a.c. it is better to use capacities instead of resistances.

If the rod forms a closed outline with the rest of the frame, and is on a continuous elastic foundation, then the circuit (Fig. 6a) must be symmetrical in relation to the longitudinal axis.

Analogues of Beams and Frames

Modelling of beams of which one or more spans are on a continuous elastic foundation is the same as in the case of simple beams. The circuit-analogue of such a beam is usually a circuit of four terminal networks.

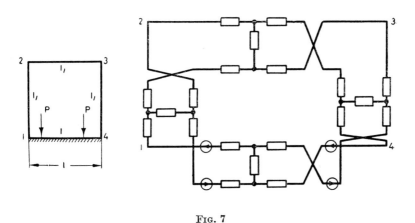

Fɪɢ. 7

When modelling frames we must take into account the presence of closed structures. We show in Fig. 7 an example of a Π-shaped frame and its electrical analogue.

Comparing the analogues described above with an analogue for a rod supported only at its ends [4] we can see that the structure of the electrical circuit-analogue is the same in both cases. Consequently, solution of the problem of bending beams and frames, positioned on continuous elastic foundations with the help of electrical analogues can be done using the same method as that for modelling simple beams and frames (without such a foundation).

References

1. L.A. GOFLIN. Electrical analogue of a beam, placed on an elastic foundation *Electricity*. No. 5. 1947.
2. A.A. UMANSKII and B.N. KUTUKOV. Calculation of solid floating bridges. Collection of articles. *Calculation of spatial constructions*. Fasc. 3. 1955.
3. G.YE. PUKHOV. *On the question of applying methods of electrical analogues into the problems of bending plane beam systems*. Publishing House of the Tomsk Polytechnical Institute. 72. Tomsk, 1952.
4. Collection of articles. *Electrical analogues of beams and frameworks*. Taganrog, 1956.
5. I.M. RABINOVICH. *Course of constructional mechanics*. Part 2. Gosstroiizdat. 1954.

INDEX

VOLUMES PUBLISHED IN THIS SERIES

(FORMERLY PERGAMON SCIENCE SERIES ELECTRONICS AND WAVES)